THE CHARLTON STANDARD CATALOGUE OF

VOLUME FOUR: LIQUOR PRODUCTS
THIRD EDITION

BY
PAT MURRAY

PUBLISHER:
W. K. CROSS

The Charlton Press
TORONTO, ONTARIO • BIRMINGHAM, MICHIGAN

COPYRIGHT NOTICE AND TRADEMARK NOTICE

DISCLAIMER

Canadian Cataloguing in Publication Data

The National Library of Canada has catalogued this publication as follows:

Murray, Pat

The Charlton standard catalogue of Wade

Biennial

3rd ed.

Previously published under title: Pre-war and more Wades.

Each issue published in 4 v.

ISSN 1203-4681
ISBN 0-88968-225-0 (v.1) ISBN 0-88968-224-0 (v.2)
ISBN 0-88968-226-7 (v.3) ISBN 0-88968-237-2 (v.4)

1. George Wade and Son - Catalogs. 2. Miniature pottery - England - Catalogs. 3. Figurines - England - Catalogs. 1. Title II. Title: Pre-war and more Wades.

NK8473.5W33M8   738.82   C96-301353-X

Printed in Canada
in the Province of Manitoba

EDITORIAL TEAM

Editor   Jean Dale
Graphic Technician   Davina Rowan

ACKNOWLEDGMENTS

Companies

Once again, many thanks to Derek Dawe and Ivan MacGee for their help in checking facts; Ralph Brough, for his background information on Wade; Joy Damsell, for her assistance in providing answers to our inquiries; Bill Walker, for his help regarding backstamps; Cynthia Risby and Jenny Wright, for their willingness to answer questions; and J. A. Stringer, for his assistance with Wade Ireland products; Adele Hall and Jenny Wright: International Wade Collectors Club.

Institutions

My appreciation to the following institutions for their research assistance:

Phillips Auctioneers and Valuers U.K.; The Potteries Specialist Auctions U.K.; British Library U.K.; Stroud Public Library, Ontario, Canada

CONTRIBUTORS TO THIS EDITION

Many thanks to the following people in England, Scotland, Canada, the United States, and New Zealand for their photographs, measurements, and backstamp information:

B Bultz, John Carter, Peter Challenger, Peter and Lesley Chisholm, David Chown and Russell Schooley (C&S Direct), Father David Cox (USA), Linda Cox (New Zealand), Joyce and David Devilbis, Ann Dullard, Dick Ellis, David Elvin, Catherine Evans, Jane and Mike Evans Yesterdays, Paul Farmer, Betty Hannigan, Al Halpern, Neil Hare, Val and Dave Holman, Pat and Connie Hoyle, Marian and Gareth Hunt, Lucy Hutchinson, Robert Jacques, Peg and Roger Johnson, Ted Joiner, Patty Keenan, Adam Less, Michael Lynch, Michael and Reva Matthews, Lynne and David Maund (Mini Bottles UK), Ron Merritt, Scott and Cathy Meyer, Joe and Augusta Miller, Phyllis Palvio, P and T Partridge, Bruce Penny, J and B Robinson (UK), Janet and Brian Robinson (New Zealand), Philip Sharp, Nicholas Slater, David Spaid (Silver State Specialities), Marco Stoof, Trevor J. Stubbs, D. Tindall, Duane and Jean Tranby, Joy and Art Turner, Kim and Derek Watson, Mr. And Mrs. Williams, Annie and Steve Windsor, Robert Wright.

And many thanks to all who helped with photographs and information but who wish to remain anonymous.

The Charlton Press

Editorial Office
2040 Yonge Street, Suite 208, Toronto, Ontario M4S 1Z9
Telephone: (416) 488-1418 Fax (416) 488-4656
Telephone: (800) 422-6042 Fax: (800) 442-1542

TABLE OF CONTENTS

HOW TO USE THIS CATALOGUE

THE PURPOSE

As with other catalogues in Charlton's Wade reference and pricing library, this publication has been designed to serve two specific purposes: first, to furnish collectors with accurate and detailed listings that will provide the essential information needed to build a rich and rewarding collection; second, to provide collectors and dealers with an indication of the current market prices of Wade liquor products.

THE LISTINGS

On the pages that follow, Wade models are listed, illustrated and priced. The measurements of the models are given in millimetres. Items such as decanters, drink pourers and water jugs are measured according to their height. For relatively flat objects such as ashtrays and dishes, the measurement listed is the diameter of a round item, the side of a square, or the longest length of a rectangle or oval. For a few items, both height and width are provided, while in other cases the capacity is provided, usually based on British standard measurements, but on occasion based on the metric system.

Although the publisher has made every attempt to obtain and photograph all models listed, several pieces, unavoidably, have not come into the publisher's possession.

A final word on the listings and the numbering of the individual liquor-related products throughout the catalogue: pending an overview by the publisher, the numbering of individual items has been simplified until the numbers or listings slow to a trickle, allowing a numbering system to be developed.

The guiding principle is the user-friendly alphabetical listing of all manufacturers who commissioned Wade potteries to produce their promotional, advertising, or special-event products. The reader need only locate the manufacturer, and under that major listing can be found the different kinds of products, from ashtrays to drink pourers and water jugs.

The collector will also be greatly assisted by an alphabetical cross-referenced index, which lists the manufacturers as well as the products under different categories, or as individual entries in the alphabetical list.

THE PRICING

The purpose of this catalogue is to give readers the most accurate, up-to-date retail prices for Wade models in the United States, Canada, and the United Kingdom.

To accomplish this, The Charlton Press continues to access an international pricing panel of Wade experts who submit prices based on both dealer and collector retail-price activity, as well as current auction results in the U.S., Canada, and the U.K. These market prices are carefully averaged to reflect accurate valuations for Wade products listed herein in each of the three markets.

A further word on pricing: as mentioned previously, this is a catalogue giving prices for items in the currency of a particular market (for example, U.S. dollars for the American market and sterling for the U.K. market). The bulk of the prices given herein are determined not by currency exchange calculations, but by actual market activity in the market concerned.

The prices published herein are for products in mint condition. Collectors are cautioned that a repaired, restored or badly scratched piece may be worth as little as 25 percent of the value of the same piece in mint condition.

A necessary word of caution: no pricing catalogue can or should be a fixed price list. This catalogue should be considered a guide only, one that shows the most current retail prices based on market demand in a particular region.

All relevant information must be known about an item to make a proper valuation. When comparing auction prices with catalogue prices, collectors and dealers should remember two important points. First, to compare "apples and apples," they must be sure that auction prices include a buyer's premium, if one is due. Prices realized for models in auction catalogues may not include this additional cost. Second, it may not be noted in the listing that an item has been restored or repaired and, as a result, the price will not be reflective of the price for the same piece in mint condition.

THE INTERNET AND PRICING

The Internet is changing the way that business is done in the collectable market. It links millions of collectors around the world to one another, allowing communication to flow freely among them. Chat rooms, antique and collector malls, Internet auctions and producer Web sites all promote the new e-commerce.

Three major effects that e-commerce will have on the collectable market are the following:

1. Collectors will deal with collectors. They will also continue with their customer/dealer relationships, but the dealer's margin will come under pressure.

2. Information on new issues, new finds, and new varieties will spread faster — and the bad news will spread even faster. Collectors' wants will be made known instantaneously to a wide universe of dealers and collectors.

3. Prices will be affected on two fronts:

    (a) Price differentials will disappear between global market areas as collectors and delivery services team up to stretch the purchasing power of the collectable dollar/pound.

    (b) As margins come under pressure, overheads being low in virtual operations, prices of the common to scarce collectable items will adjust downward to compensate. The rare and extremely rare items will move up as a result of their exposure.

INTRODUCTION

A BRIEF OVERVIEW

Although the advertising and promotional products manufactured by Wade tend to fall into broad and well-defined categories, there are also more unusual products and some nostalgic/historical items that set a change of pace for the collector.

The most frequently commissioned items tended to be ashtrays, decanters, drink pourers, water jugs, pump handles, and specialty bottles along with the more standard derivatives such as cruets and menu holders.

However, other products do crop up: loving cups with different motifs such as fruits and flowers, the wassailing theme, or remembrance of the men who defended Great Britain. There are bar lamps, instantly recreating the homey ambiance of the corner pub. The collector will find horn decanters and Chinese New Year decanters, novelty drink pourers, and My Fair Ladies figurines who daintily and demurely held their "liqueur," as well as a sprinkling of unique sports commemorative items.

For something truly different, look to the "Thistle and Rose" chess set, emblematic of the struggle between the royal houses of Scotland and England, or to "Pomona, Goddess of the Orchards."

HISTORY

An extraordinary number of people from all walks of life are enthusiastic collectors of the Wade potteries' products.

What boosts the "collectability quotient" of Wade products in the eyes of many collectors is the range of products available and the craftsmanship and quality of the individual pieces.

The Wade potteries manufacture an especially hard porcelain body produced by a mixture of ball clays, china clay, flint, feldspar and talc, along with a variety of imported ingredients. Utilized to best effect are both underglaze decoration — achieved by the application of colour to the model and spraying with a clear glaze that lets colours show through after firing — and on-glaze decoration, whose processes of enamelling, gilding and transfer printing are applied after glazing and firing.

One must also consider an indefinable quality, an environment where new techniques and imagination create new product lines that either captivate with their charm or impress with durability, craftsmanship and quality of a kind that our world, with its orientation towards disposable products, does not see regularly anymore.

Originally, the main thrust of the Wade potteries was to fulfill practical commercial needs by manufacturing items such as gas burners for domestic lighting, then bobbins, thread guides and tiles. The rapid changes of the middle decades of the twentieth century created different demands that had to be met. When World War II broke out, only the production of essential ceramics was allowed by the government. Giftware production was discontinued, and part of the buildings and storage facilities functioned as emergency food stores during the war years. When peace finally arrived, it was imperative to restore and replace the essential ceramics destroyed by the bombing.

The shadow of war persisted for a while, judging by the fact that in the 1960s the company made cone heads for guided missiles. But by the early 1950s, the George Wade pottery was producing small collectable figures and animals.

To put things into perspective, it must be remembered that even in the 1930s, when Wade consisted of three potteries — A. J. Wade Ltd., George Wade and Son Ltd., and Wade Heath and Co. Ltd, with Wade Ulster (Ireland) being acquired in the mid-1940s — the company had always produced a modest amount of giftware.

The years between 1953 and 1969 saw Wade Heath and Co. Ltd. working in tandem with Reginald Corfield (Sales) Ltd. of Redhill, Surrey (with the trademark "Regicor London"), and marketing a range of promotional and point-of-sale advertising ware. Frequently, original water jugs and ashtrays were designed for clients and retained as exclusive shapes for particular brands. Produced by Wade Heath at the Royal Victoria Pottery in Burslem, these were always quality products. Although the major affiliation for this cooperative venture was with manufacturers in the brewing, distilling and tobacco industries, it was not restricted to these spheres of enterprise.

The ensuing years brought changes, with a restructuring in 1958. The three English Wade potteries became Wade Potteries Ltd., then later were renamed Wade PLC. Wade Ulster in turn became Wade Ireland in 1966.

The association with Reginald Corfield was discontinued in October 1969, and Wade Heath focused on establishing its own product, design and marketing company, Wade PDM, with "PDM" denoting "point of sale, design and marketing."

Wade PDM's specialty was advertising products for the industries that had been the mainstay of the "Regicor London" trademark, but it was not exclusively engaged in these areas, having evolved into one of the leading suppliers of advertising ware in the U.K.

Further business developments resulted in Wade PLC metamorphosing into Wade Ceramics Ltd. Under the auspices of Beauford PLC, it is still in operation. Wade Ireland, renamed Seagoe Ceramics, continued the manufacture of domestic tableware until 1993, and then its production was dedicated to meeting the need for industrial ceramics.

Those who have recently become acquainted with Wade collectables, as well as long-time aficionados, know that Wade produced a wide array of ceramics and earthenware items: tableware, commemorative ware, figures, animals, birds, and "Whimsies." Additionally, the many decades of affiliation with industry, in particular the brewing and distilling industries, created a diverse wealth of products that range from ashtrays, anniversary and ship's decanters, drink pourers, and loving cups to unique display items that can meaningfully enrich a collection.

IDENTIFICATION

With some exceptions, the items in this catalogue were commissioned by liquor companies to publicize their company names or advertise particular brands. For the various brewers, distillers, wine sellers and liqueur manufacturers, it made good marketing sense that some of the most popular products they commissioned were items like drink pourers and water jugs. These were on display at bars, pubs, hotels, and similar establishments, suitable and appropriate settings that reflected well on both the manufacturers and the establishments. In the neighbourhood-oriented, informal atmosphere of many British pubs, the companies and the standard products that carried their brand names — drink pourers and water jugs — were at home, and this connection proclaimed tradition, reliability, and quality.

Drink Pourers

Drink pourers are fairly compact, which eases the burden of housing a sizeable collection in an ordinary home, and perhaps that is one of the reasons that pourers are some people's favourite collectable. A great variety were manufactured, with differences in shapes, decorative elements, and fittings.

Some drink pourers are all porcelain, while in others only the button is porcelain. Pourers made of porcelain can be fitted with either a metal venting tube and metal spout or a plastic venting tube and porcelain or plastic spout. The listings indicate the tube composition when it is known.

Pourer composition is linked in some respects to a date of manufacture, or more precisely, it can limit the date of manufacture to a certain era. It is well known that all-porcelain pourers and those with metal tubes and spouts are the early versions, and some of these older pourers may also have have a metal dust cover on the pourer tube. Plastic tubes and spouts were a later feature: Wade PDM has manufactured a variety of plastic pourers since 1994.

Porcelain buttons can have the same wording and illustration on the front and back or have one type on the front and another on the back, e.g. "King George IV Scotch Whisky" lettering with a portrait on the front, and on the back a portrait only. The lettering can also differ, with the product name being in upper case, lower case or a combination of upper and lower case. Some pourers advertise two different liquors, one brand on the front and another on the back, or may advertise several different brands on the front only.

Pourer Shapes

AP1	All-porcelain, circle on short neck, 97mm
AP2	All-porcelain, circle on medium neck, 117mm
AP3	All-porcelain, circle on long neck, 130mm
AP4	All-porcelain, circle on medium wide neck, 117mm
AP5	All-porcelain, rectangle on medium neck, 117mm
BIG1	Porcelain round button with flat base, 62 mm, metal fittings
C52A	Porcelain rectangular button with clipped shoulders, 40 mm x 48 mm, metal or plastic fittings
C53	Porcelain round button with flat base, 44 mm, metal fittings
C53A	Porcelain round button with flat top and base, 44mm, plastic fittings
C54	Porcelain rectangular button with clipped shoulders on the bottom, 60mm, metal or plastic fittings
C57	Porcelain rectangular button with rounded top and clipped shoulders on the top and bottom, 60mm, metal fittings
C62	Porcelain square button with clipped corners, 47mm
5455/1	Porcelain angular button, 47 mm, plastic fittings

Water Jugs

Pub water jugs that advertise various alcoholic beverages were produced in a multitude of styles: tall and rounded, short and rounded, tall and square-sided, short and square-sided, oblong, and the traditional harvest type, as well as the exclusive shapes of the Beefeater Gin castle-shaped jug and the Worthington E-shaped jug. They also have two types of spouts, open and closed (which is called an ice-check spout), and two different handles, applied and recessed (moulded in with the body of the jug).

Containers

1. Some dates in this section are approximate only, as no information on production start or end dates is available.

2. When liquor containers were originally sold, they were filled with liquor, but most containers bought at collector shows are empty; therefore, the prices listed here are for empty containers. Decorative decanters with unbroken seals, in their original packaging and containing the original liquor, are worth considerably more.

BACKSTAMPS

Wade Regicor and Wade PDM Backstamps

Wade Regicor and Wade PDM backstamps are found in black, blue, yellow, white, green, red, and gold. The colour of the backstamps varied in order to contrast with the base colour of the models. The dating of a product is determined not by the colour of the backstamp, but by its style.

1953-1962: "Wade Regicor, London England" in between two upright rows of nine laurel-type leaves, large size (18 mm x 20 mm)

1962-1968: "Wade Regicor, London England" in between two upright rows of nine laurel-type leaves, small size (13 mm x 13 mm)

1968-1969: "Reginald Corfield Limited Redhill Surrey" printed in a circle, with "Wade Regicor England" printed through the circle

1969-1984: "Wade pdm England" printed in a circle (this was the first Wade PDM backstamp)

1984-1990: "Wade p d m England"

1990-1996: "Wade P D M England" or "Wade P D M Made in England" within two red lines, one thick and the other thin

Private Backstamps

Some backstamps do not correspond to those listed above. They incorporate information about the liquor company and may not indicate that the item was produced by Wade.

Drink Pourers

A large number of drink pourers have been produced by Wade since 1955. Some of the first pourers issued are backstamped "Wade Regicor," but most are unmarked. From 1969 onwards, pourers were produced through Wade PDM. The backstamp, if any, is on the neck of the pourer, obscured by a cork that secures the pourer in the bottle. The cork is usually glued in place, making it difficult to see whether there is a Wade backstamp underneath. Where a backstamp has been confirmed, it is noted in the text.

INSURING YOUR MODELS

As with any of your other valuables, making certain your models are protected is very important. It is paramount that you display or store any porcelain items in a secure place, preferably one safely away from traffic in the home.

Your models are most likely covered under your basic homeowner's policy. There are generally three kinds of such policies: standard, broad and comprehensive. Each has its own specific deductible and terms.

Under a general policy, your models are considered part of the contents and are covered for all of the perils covered under the contractual terms of your policy (fire, theft, water damage, and so on).

There is usually an extra premium attached to insure models against accidental breakage by or carelessness of the owner. This is sometimes referred to as a "fine arts" rider. You are advised to contact your insurance professional to get all the answers.

To help protect yourself, it is critical that you take inventory of your models and have colour photographs taken of all your pieces. This is the surest method of clearly establishing, for the police and your insurance company, which items have been lost or destroyed. It is also the easiest way to establish their replacement value.

LIQUOR PRODUCTS

ABBOT'S CHOICE SCOTCH WHISKY
JOHN McEWAN & CO. LTD.

ASHTRAYS, 1962-1969

The No. 2 ashtray is decorated with a transfer print of an abbot.

Backstamp: A. "Wade Regicor London England," laurel leaves, small size
B. "Reginald Corfield Limited Redhill Surrey," "Wade Regicor England"

No.	Description	Colourways	Shape/Size	U.S.$	Can.$	U.K.£
1.	Ashtray	Tan; black print, lettering "The Abbot's Choice Scotch Whisky"	Round/127	15.00	20.00	8.00
2.	Ashtray	White; red/black lettering "Abbot Ale, Harvest Ale"	Square/140	15.00	20.00	8.00

DECANTERS, c.1980 AND 1987

This decanter was first produced c.1980 in a honey-amber glaze, with the volume of the contents listed on the label in fluid ounces. In 1987 a second bottle was issued, which was labeled in centilitres.

Two types of the Abbot Bottle were produced:

Type 1: Was produced in a honey-amber glaze with brown hands, with five sections on the longest end of his cord belt. Size: 214 mm collar to base.

Type 2: Was produced in a burnt umber glaze with creamy white hands, and six sections on the longest end of his cord belt. Size: 212 mm collar to base.

Backstamp: A. Embossed "Made Exclusively for the Abbots Choice Scotch Whisky John McEwan & Co. Ltd. Leith, Scotland"
B. Embossed "Made Exclusively for the Abbots Choice Scotch Whisky John McEwan & Co. Ltd. Leith, Scotland Liquor Bottle Scotland"

No.	Description	Colourways	Size	U.S.$	Can.$	U.K.£
1.	Type 1 (ounces)	Honey-amber; brown hands; five sections on cord belt	255	120.00	155.00	55.00
2.	Type 2 (centilitres)	Burnt umber; white hands; six sections on cord belt	253	120.00	155.00	55.00

AKITA SHOCHU

DRINK POURER

This pourer, intended for a sake bottle, has a straight base and is Wade PDM shape number C53.

Photograph not available
at press time

Backstamp: Unmarked

No.	Description	Colourways	Shape/Size	U.S.$	Can.$	U.K.£
1.	Drink Pourer	Black porcelain tube; gold/red lettering "Akita Shochu"	Circular/41	30.00	35.00	15.00

ANSELLS BEER

ASHTRAYS, 1955-1990

Ashtray No. 2 is decorated with a transfer print of a squirrel.

Ansells The Better Beer

Backstamp: **A.** "Wade Regicor, London England," laurel leaves, large size
B. "Wade p d m England"

No.	Description	Colourways	Shape/Size	U.S.$	Can.$	U.K.£
1.	Ashtray	Cream; black lettering "Ansells Beer"	Oval/171	15.00	20.00	8.00
2.	Ashtray	Yellow; black/gold print; black/red lettering "Ansells"	Oval/190	15.00	20.00	8.00
3.	Ashtray	Yellow; black lettering "Ansells The Better Beer"	Square/140	15.00	20.00	8.00

ASPREY & CO. LONDON

DECANTER, c.1938

This decanter, which is the top half of a Scotsman on an octagonal box base, was originally produced for Asprey & Co. by Royal Doulton. Many liquor companies commissioned the Royal Doulton, Spode and Beswick potteries to produce their special decanters. When a repeat of the decanter was needed and the original pottery could not take the order, the commissioner turned to other potteries such as Wade.

If a new shape was not required, the same mould (which was owned by the distiller) would then be used by Wade. Other examples of decanters from the same mould or similar mould but produced by different potteries can be seen in the Bells Bottle, Chivas Bottle and Beneagles Eagle decanter which can be found with Royal Doulton, Spode, Beswick and Wade backstamps.

Backstamp: Hand written "Wade England for Asprey & Co. London Reg No. 675852"

No.	Description	Colourways	Size	U.S.$	Can.$	U.K.£
1.	Decanter	Dark red tam; black and white check band; green-black jacket; black base	242	500.00	675.00	300.00

BACARDI RUM

ASHTRAY, 1984-1990

Photograph not available
at press time

Backstamp: A. "Wade p d m England"

No.	Description	Colourways	Shape/Size	U.S.$	Can.$	U.K.£
1.	Ashtray	White; red lettering "Bacardi Rum"	Rectangular/210	13.00	18.00	5.00

WATER JUG, 1968-1969

Backstamp: Printed circular "Reginald Corfield Limited, Redhill Surrey," with "Regicor Wade England" through the circle

No.	Description	Colourways	Size	U.S.$	Can.$	U.K.£
1.	Water Jug, open spout	Pale blue; red/yellow Bat print; black/yellow lettering "Bacardi Rum The Spirit of Adventure"	Round/163	32.00	40.00	20.00

BADGER BEER

ASHTRAYS, BAR LAMP AND WATER JUG, 1955-1990

Styles No. 1 and 2 of these ashtrays are decorated with a transfer print of a badger.

The water jug was produced between 1955 and 1962. It has an open spout and also has a print of a badger on it.

Backstamp: A. "Wade Regicor, London England," laurel leaves, large size
B. "Reginald Corfield Limited Redhill Surrey," "Wade Regicor England"
C. "Wade p d m England"

No.	Description	Colourways	Shape/Size	U.S.$	Can.$	U.K.£
1.	Ashtray	Blue; yellow print, lettering "Badger Beer"	Oval/216	10.00	15.00	5.00
2.	Ashtray	Blue; yellow print, lettering "Badger Beer"	Square/135	15.00	20.00	8.00
3.	Ashtray	Blue; yellow lettering "Badger Beer"	Square/140	15.00	20.00	8.00
4.	Bar Lamp	Blue; yellow print, lettering "Badger Beer"	height/192	78.00	100.00	45.00
5.	Water Jug	Blue; yellow print, lettering "Badger Beer"	Round/170	28.00	34.00	14.00

THE BAKER AND OVEN

WATER JUG

This water jug is unusual in that it is advertising "The Baker and Oven," a public house name rather than a liquor product.

Backstamp: Circular transfer printed "Reginald Corfield Ltd Redhill Surrey - Wade Regicor England" (c. 1968-c.1969)

No.	Description	Colourways	Size	U.S.$	Can.$	U.K.£
1.	Water Jug	Tan brown; black print/lettering "The Baker and Oven"	Rect./145	30.00	35.00	15.00

BALLANTINE'S SCOTCH WHISKY

ASHTRAY, DECANTERS AND WATER JUGS, 1969-1984

The ashtray and the style No. 5 water jug are decorated with a transfer print of the company's crest. The No. 2 whisky decanter, which has two handles on its neck, was originally produced by Wade Heath in 1969, with later production moved to Wade Ireland. The water jugs have ice-check spouts.

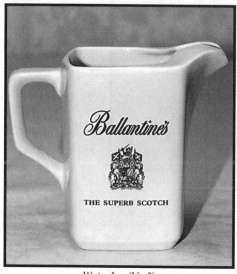
Water Jug (No.3)

Decanter (No.3)

Backstamp: **A.** "Reginald Corfield Limited Redhill Surrey", "Wade Regicor England"
B. "Wade pdm England"
C. Gold printed "Genuine Wade Porcelain"

No.	Description	Colourways	Shape/Size	U.S.$	Can.$	U.K.£
1.	Ashtray	Black; multi-coloured print; black lettering "Ballantine's the Superb Scotch"	Square/108	10.00	15.00	5.00
2.	Decanter	Black; gold lettering "Ballantine's Very Old Scotch Whisky"	Round/75	50.00	65.00	30.00
3.	Decanter	Cobalt blue; gold lettering "Ballantine's Very Old Scotch Whisky Aged 21 Years"	Rectangular/235	50.00	65.00	30.00
4.	Water Jug	Yellow; red/black lettering "Ballantine's Whisky"	Rectangular/150	30.00	35.00	15.00
5.	Water Jug	White; multi-coloured print; black lettering "Ballantine's The Superb Scotch"	Rectangular/153	30.00	35.00	15.00

BALVENIE SCOTCH WHISKY

MINIATURE DECANTER

Backstamp: Red printed "Wade Made in England" plus label which reads "Contains 50ml The Balvenie 43% vol Single malt Scotch Whisky Aged 10 years"

No.	Description	Colourways	Shape/Size	U.S.$	Can.$	U.K.£
1.	Decanter	White; blue; red; black lettering "The Balvenie Single Malt Whisky aged 10 years"	50 x 133	600.00	800.00	395.00

BANKS BEER

ASHTRAY, c.1967-1969

Backstamp: **A**. "Reginald Corfield Limited Redhill Surrey," "Wade Regicor England"
              B. "Wade pdm England"

No.	Description	Colourways	Shape/Size	U.S.$	Can.$	U.K.£
1.	Ashtray	White; black print; red/black lettering "Banks Beer is Best"	Round /120	15.00	20.00	8.00

BARREL TANKARDS

The Wade Barrel Tankard has the name "Banks" added to the front.

Backstamp: Red printed "Wade England"

No.	Description	Colourways	Size	U.S.$	Can.$	U.K.£
1.	Tankard	Amber; gold bands/handle; red lettering "Banks"	Pint /130	25.00	30.00	12.00
2.	Tankard	Amber; silver bands/handle; black lettering " Banks"	Pint /130	25.00	30.00	12.00

13

BARNSLEY BITTER

ASHTRAY

This cube shaped ashtray has the Oakwell Brewery logo of oak leaves and acorns on the sides, and has flat corners.

Backstamp: Printed "Wade Regicor London England," laurel leaf frame (large size 18 x 20 mm 1953-1962)

No.	Description	Colourways	Size	U.S.$	Can.$	U.K.£
1.	Ashtray	White; multi-coloured acorns print; red lettering "Barnsley Bitter Brewed Only at Oakwell"	53 x 105	12.00	15.00	6.00

BARON OTARD COGNAC

WATER JUG

This water jug has an open spout.

Backstamp: Printed circular "Wade pdm England" (pdm separated 1984-1990)

No.	Description	Colourways	Size	U.S.$	Can.$	U.K.£
1.	Water Jug	Black; gold rim/lettering "Estd 1795 Cognac Baron Otard Otard-The Only Cognac Aged At The Chateau de Cognac"	150	35.00	45.00	22.00

BASS BEER

The embossed Bass cask ale ashtray No.10 has the words "Bass Breweries Ltd. Burton-on-Trent. Brewers of Fine Ales Since 1777" around the rim.

"Bass For Men" (No.9)

"Bass Special" (No.11)

"Bass Light" (No.13)

"Great Stuff This Bass" (No.14)

Backstamp:
- **A.** "Wade Regicor, London England", laurel leaves, large size
- **B.** "Wade pdm England"
- **C.** "Wade p d m England"
- **D.** "Wade P D M Made in England"
- **E.** Printed "Wade PDM Made in England" (PDM separate 1984-1990)

No.	Description	Colourways	Shape/Size	U.S.$	Can.$	U.K.£
1.	Ashtray	Black; red lettering "Bass Cask Ale"	Oval/171	15.00	20.00	8.00
2.	Ashtray	Black; red/gold lettering "Bass Our Finest Ale"	Oval/171	15.00	20.00	8.00
3.	Ashtray	Mottled black/light brown; brown lettering "Bass"	Rectang./153	10.00	15.00	5.00
4.	Ashtray	White/red; red print, lettering "Bass"	Round/133	25.00	30.00	12.00
5.	Ashtray	White/red; red lettering "Bass For Men"	Round/133	25.00	30.00	12.00
6.	Ashtray	White; gold rim; red/black lettering "Bass Export"	Round/228	10.00	15.00	5.00
7.	Ashtray	Black; red/gold lettering "Bass"	Square/159	10.00	15.00	5.00
8.	Ashtray	Mustard yellow; black/red lettering "Great Stuff This Bass"	Square/177	10.00	15.00	5.00
9.	Ashtray	White; red lettering "Bass For Men"	Square/140	10.00	15.00	5.00

No.	Name	Colourways	Size	U.S.$	Can.$	U.K.£
10.	Ashtray	Black; gold lettering "Bass Cask Ale" "Bass Breweries Ltd. Burton-on-Trent. Brewers of Fine Ales Since 1777"	Oval/190	25.00	30.00	12.00
11.	Ashtray	Cream; blue/white label; red lettering, "Bass Special"	Rectang./210	15.00	20.00	8.00
12.	Ashtray	White; red bands/triangle; blue lettering "Bass Special"	Round/218	15.00	20.00	8.00
13.	Ashtray	Cobalt blue; white/blue print; red/gold lettering "Bass Light"	Square/165	12.00	18.00	8.00
14.	Ashtray	Mustard yellow; black/red lettering "Great Stuff This Bass"	Square/155	10.00	15.00	5.00

CRUET, 1968-1969

The mustard pot in this set is the same square shape as the salt and pepper, with the addition of a lift-off lid.

Salt Cruet (No.2)

Backstamp: "Reginald Corfield Limited Redhill Surrey," " Wade Regicor England"

No.	Name	Colourways	Size	U.S.$	Can.$	U.K.£
1.	Pepper	White; blue/red lettering Bass Naturally	80	8.00	10.00	3.00
2.	Salt	White; blue/red lettering Bass Naturally	80	8.00	10.00	3.00
3.	Mustard pot	White; blue/red lettering Bass Naturally	76	8.00	10.00	3.00

WATER JUG, 1969-1984

This water jug is round with an open spout and is decorated with a print of hops.

Photograph not available
at press time

Backstamp: "Wade pdm England"

No.	Description	Colourways	Size	U.S.$	Can.$	U.K.£
1.	Water Jug	White; green/yellow print; multi-coloured lettering "Bass Label"	177	30.00	35.00	15.00

BEAUFORD PLC

DECANTERS, 1994

One hundred of these decanters were produced for the staff of Beauford PLC (the owners of Wade Ceramics) for Christmas 1994. Another 400 decanters were produced for Christmas 1995, 350 for the George Wade staff and 50 for Beauford Engineering. The decanter is shaped like a bottle oven (an old pottery kiln) and has the names of the six Staffordshire pottery towns embossed around the bottom edge: "Burslem—Stoke—Hanley—Fenton—Longton— Tunstall."

Backstamp: A. Embossed "Potteries Decanter by Wade for Beauford PLC"
B. Embossed "Potteries Decanter by Wade"

No.	Description	Colourways	Size	U.S.$	Can.$	U.K.£
1.	Christmas 1994	Grey	200	100.00	125.00	65.00
2.	Christmas 1995	Dark green	200	100.00	125.00	65.00

BEEFEATER GIN
BURROUGHS

ASHTRAYS, 1955-1984

Styles No. 2, 3 and 4 of these ashtrays are decorated with prints of the Yeomen of the Guard, better known as Beefeaters.

Square ashtray

Ashtray with clipped corners

Round Beefeater Gin Ashtray

Backstamp: A. "Wade Regicor, London England," laurel leaves, large size
B. "Reginald Corfield Limited Redhill Surrey," "Wade Regicor England"
C. "Wade pdm England"

No.	Description	Colourways	Shape/Size	U.S.$	Can.$	U.K.£
1.	Ashtray	White; red lettering "Beefeater London Gin"	Round/205	15.00	20.00	8.00
2.	Ashtray	White; multi-coloured Beefeater print; red lettering "Beefeater Gin"	Round/125	10.00	15.00	8.00
3.	Ashtray	Yellow; multi-coloured print; red lettering "Beefeater Dry Gin"	Square/120	15.00	20.00	8.00
4.	Ashtray	White; multi-coloured print; red lettering "Beefeater The Gin of England"	Square/140	10.00	15.00	5.00
5.	Ashtray	Yellow; multi-coloured print; red lettering "Beefeater Dry Gin"	Square/120 clipped corners	15.00	20.00	8.00

DRINK POURERS, 1966-1969

The first Beefeater pourer had a long neck and was all white. Subsequent long neck pourers were multi-coloured, with grey beards, and the later short neck pourers are multi-coloured with white beards. The wording on the top of the hat of the long neck and short neck versions differ: on the long neck, and the first of the short necks, the name "Burroughs Beefeater Gin" is printed, but on the later short necks only "Beefeater Gin" appears. The decoration on the hat band also differs with each version. These hand-painted "Beefeater Gin" pourers were first produced in 1966 for Burroughs Beefeater Gin. Style No. 1 has a large hat and a porcelain neck below the cork, with the backstamp on the neck; No. 2 has a large hat, with the backstamp on the ruff; and 3 and 4 have small hat, with the backstamp also on the ruff. An unusual pourer is No. 10, in that it has a plastic screw cap bottle top attached to the neck of the pourer. It is found in its original box, which has "The Beefeater Pourer Made in England" printed on it in gold letters.

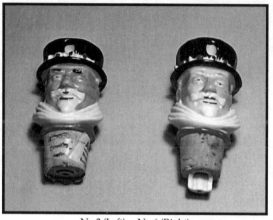

No.2 (Left)   No.6 (Right)   No.2 (Left)   No.6 (Right)

Backstamp: **A.** Embossed "England" on neck
B. Printed "Made in England" on neck
C. Printed "Wade Regicor Made in England," laurel leaf frame (small size 13 x 13 mm 1962-late 1968 on neck
D. Printed "Wade Regicor Made in England" on neck
E. Printed "Wade Regicor Made in UK" on neck
F. Printed "Wade Regicor Made in Great Britain" on ruff
G. Printed "Wade Made in England" on ruff

Long and Short Neck, Porcelain

No.	Description	Colourways	Size	U.S.$	Can.$	U.K.£
1.	Large hat, long neck	All white	115	50.00	65	40.00
2.	Small hat, long neck	Black hat; eyebrows; pink face; dark grey hair beard and ruff; black lettering "Burroughs Beefeater Gin"	115	45.00	60.00	35.00
3.	Small hat, long neck	Black hat; eyebrows; pink face; dark grey hair beard; white ruff; black lettering "Burroughs Gin"	115	50.00	60.00	35.00
4.	Small hat, long neck	Black hat; brown eyebrows; pink face; dark grey hair, beard, eyebrows; white ruff; black lettering "Burroughs Beefeater Gin"	120	50.00	60.00	35.00
5.	Small hat, long neck	Black hat; brown eyebrows; pink face; dark grey hair, beard; white ruff; black lettering "Burroughs Beefeater Gin"	120	50.00	60.00	35.00
6.	Large hat, short neck	Black hat, eyebrows; pink face, light grey hair, eyebrows; white beard, ruff; black lettering "Burroughs Beefeater Gin"	80	50.00	60.00	35.00
7.	Large hat, short neck	Black hat; pink face; light grey hair; eyebrows; white beard; ruff; black lettering "Burroughs Beefeater Gin"	87	50.00	60.00	35.00

Drink Pourer (No. 10)

Drink Pourer (No.11)

Drink Pourer (No.12)

Drink Pourer (No. 13)

Drink Pourer (No. 14)

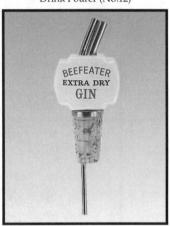

Drink Pourer (No. 15)

Backstamp: Impressed "C52A" under porcelain button, not seen unless pourer is taken apart

No.	Description	Colourways	Size	U.S.$	Can.$	U.K.£
8.	Small hat, short neck	Black hat; pink face; dark grey hair, eyebrows; white beard, ruff; black lettering" Beefeater Gin"	77	50.00	60.00	35.00
9.	Small hat, short neck	Black hat; dark pink face; dark grey hair, eyebrows white beard, ruff; black lettering "Beefeater Gin"	77	50.00	60.00	35.00
10.	Beefeater, short hat/ plastic screw cap	Black hat, eyebrows; pink face; dark grey hair;	80	50.00	65.00	40.00
11.	Drink Pourer	White; plastic spout, tube; red border/lettering "Beefeater The Gin of England"	40 x 48 Octag. C52A	25.00	30.00	12.00
12.	Drink Pourer	White; metal spout, tube; red border/lettering "Beefeater Gin"	40 x 48 Octag. C52A	25.00	30.00	12.00
13.	Drink Pourer	Red/White; metal spout, tube; white lettering "Beefeater Gin"	40 x 48 Octag. C52A	25.00	30.00	12.00
14.	Drink Pourer	White; metal spout, tube; red border/lettering "Beefeater Gin"	40 x 48 Octag. C52A	25.00	30.00	12.00
15.	Drink Pourer	White/beige; metal spout, tube; lettering "Beefeater Extra Dry Gin"	40 x 48 Octag. C52A	25.00	30.00	12.00

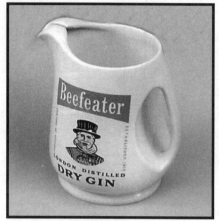

Beefeater (No. 1)

Beefeater (No.2)

Beefeater/Castle (No.4)

Beefeater (No. 5)

Backstamp: A. "Reginald Corfield Limited Redhill Surrey," " Wade Regicor England"
B. "Wade pdm England"

No.	Description	Colourways	Size	U.S.$	Can.$	U.K.£
1.	Water Jug	White; multi-coloured print; white/red lettering "Beefeater London Distilled Dry Gin"	153	25.00	30.00	12.00
2.	Water Jug	White; multi-coloured Beefeater and Tower of London print; red lettering "Beefeater Gin"	153	35.00	45.00	20.00
3.	Water Jug	White; multi-coloured Beefeater print; red lettering "Beefeater Gin"	153	35.00	45.00	20.00
4.	Water Jug	White; multi-coloured print; red/black lettering "Beefeater The Gin of England"	146	35.00	45.00	23.00
5.	Water Jug	White; multi-coloured print; red lettering "Beefeater Gin"	146	35.00	45.00	23.00

BELL'S WHISKY
ARTHUR BELL AND SONS LTD; UNITED DISTILLERS UK PLC

ASHTRAYS, 1965-1996

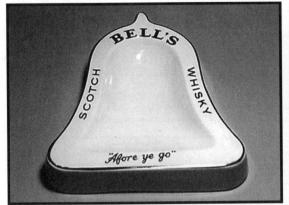

Bell's Scotch Whisky "Afore ye go" (No.2)   Bell's Scotch Whisky Extra Special (No.4)

Backstamp: **A.** "Wade Regicor, London England," laurel leaves, small size
B. "Wade pdm England"
C. "Wade p d m England"

No.	Description	Colourways	Shape/Size	U.S.$	Can.$	U.K.£
1.	Ashtray	White; gold lines; red lettering "Bell's Scotch Whisky 'Afore Ye Go'"	Bell/195	30.00	35.00	15.00
2.	Ashtray	Cream; black/red lettering "Bell's Scotch Whisky 'Afore Ye Go'"	Bell/195	30.00	35.00	15.00
3.	Ashtray	Cream; brown/red/cream lettering "Bell's Extra Special"	Bell/228	30.00	35.00	15.00
4.	Ashtray	Cream; brown/red/cream lettering "Bell's Old Scotch Whisky Extra Special"	Round/177	10.00	15.00	5.00

DECANTERS

For over thirty years, George Wade and Son, now Wade Ceramics, has collaborated with Arthur Bell & Sons Ltd. in producing the bell-shaped decanters with which collectors are so familiar. Bells is now owned by United Distillers.

A number of special decanters were issued and were only available at the Cherrybank Gardens visitors centre or were available only to Bell's Company officials and staff and they are listed on pages 24, 25 and 26.

Church-Bell Decanters, 1988-1996

In 1988 Bell's changed its decanter design from that resembling a hand bell to what can best be described as a church bell. The new bell shape has a shorter neck, a three-tiered shoulder and a banded skirt. The first decanter issued in the new shape was for the birth of Princess Beatrice on August 8, 1988 (see Commemorative section in *The Charlton Standard Catalogue of Wade Vol. One: General Issues 3rd Edition*.) From this date on, all Bell's decanters were produced in the new shape.

Bell's 12-year-old Scotch whisky came in No. 3 and No. 4 style. They have a recessed shield on the centre of the top shoulder, in which there is a gold label with the words "12 years old" in black lettering. Some of the Bell's decanters were available from the Wade ceramics shop and offered to members of the Wade Collectors Club during 1999, for a price ranging from £12.50 and £14.95.

75 cl (No. 2)

12-Yr.-Old Whisky, black cap (No. 3)

Backstamp: "Genuine Wade Porcelain"

No.	Description	Colourways	Size	U.S.$	Can.$	U.K.£
1.	Bell, 5 Cl	Gold cap; tan/cream bottle	Miniature/ 85	30.00	35.00	15.00
2.	Bell, 75 Cl	Gold cap; tan/cream bottle	200	20.00	30.00	10.00
3.	12-Yr.-Old Whisky	Black cap; dark brown/brown bottle	200	50.00	70.00	25.00
4.	12-Yr.-Old Whisky	Gold cap; dark blue bottle	200	50.00	70.00	25.00

Church-Bell Chinese New Year, 1990-1996

In 1990 Bell's introduced a series of decanters filled with 12-year-old whisky and decorated with a print of the animal that represents each year: however, only the Sheep and Monkey decanters were actually produced. Although Chinese New Year is in February, these decanters were sold during the Christmas season. They have a recessed shield on the centre of the top shoulder, in which there is a gold label with the words "12 years old" in black lettering.

Photograph not available
at press time

Backstamp: "Genuine Wade Porcelain"

No.	Description	Colourways	Size	U.S.$	Can.$	U.K.£
1.	1991 Sheep	Gold cap; black bottle; gold print	200	30.00	40.00	20.00
2.	1992 Monkey	Gold cap; black bottle; gold print	200	35.00	50.00	25.00

Church-Bell Christmas Decanters, 1988-1998

Bell's issued its first Christmas decanter in 1988. The print on the 1988 decanter is of Christmas carollers; a winter scene is on the 1989 decanter. In 1990 the first Christmas-bell decanter with a series theme was introduced. Each year a decanter was issued with a transfer decoration depicting the process of distilling whisky. The 1994 decanter was the first decanter filled with Bell's new 8-year-old blended whisky. It can be distinguished from the other Christmas decanters by a gold band around the rim with "8 yr old" printed on it.

Christmas 1989

Christmas 1991

Christmas 1996

Backstamp: "Genuine Wade Porcelain"

No.	Description	Colourways	Size	U.S.$	Can.$	U.K.£
1.	Christmas 1988	"We Wish You a Merry Christmas"	200	75.00	100.00	50.00
2.	Christmas 1989	"Perth Scotland Winter 1895"	200	30.00	40.00	20.00
3.	Christmas 1990	"The Art of Distilling," brewery print	200	30.00	40.00	20.00
4.	Christmas 1991	"The Art of Distilling," Oast House print	200	30.00	40.00	20.00
5.	Christmas 1992	"The Cooper's Art"	200	30.00	40.00	20.00
6.	Christmas 1993	"The Maltman's Art"	200	30.00	40.00	20.00
7.	Christmas 1994	"The Blender's Art"	200	30.00	40.00	20.00
8.	Christmas 1995	"The Cellar Man's Art"	200	60.00	80.00	30.00
9.	Christmas 1996	"The Ingredients of Quality," sheaf of barley		60.00	80.00	30.00
10.	Christmas 1997	"Map of Scotland"	200	60.00	80.00	30.00
11.	Christmas 1998	"The Ingredients of Quality," leaping salmon	70 cl/200	60.00	80.00	30.00

Church Bell United Distillers Broxburn 31st December 1995

Backstamp: Gold crest and red script "31st December 1995 Commercial Division"

No.	Description	Colourways	Size	U.S.$	Can.$	U.K.£
1.	Decanter	Brown/tan; black lettering "United Distillers Broxburn 31st December 1995 Commercial Division"	200	45.00	55.00	20.00

Hand Bell 150 Years of Bells Scotch Whisky, 1825-1975

Photograph not available
at press time

No.	Description	Colourways	Size	U.S.$	Can.$	U.K.£
1.	Decanter	Tan/gold; black, red/gold label, lettering "1825-1975 150 Years of Bell's Scotch Whisky"	250	Unknown		

Hand Bell Cherrybank Head Office Opening, 1980

Photograph not available
at press time

No.	Description	Colourways	Size	U.S.$	Can.$	U.K.£
1.	Decanter	Tan/gold; multi coloured print, lettering "Cherrybank Head Office Opening"	250	Unknown		

Hand Bell Queen's Award For Export Achievement, 21st April 1983

Photograph not available
at press time

No.	Description	Colourways	Size	U.S.$	Can.$	U.K.£
	Decanter	White; red, black/blue label, lettering "Queen's Award for Export Achievement"	250	Unknown		

Hand Bell Gleneagles Hotel, 1989

Photograph not available
at press time

Backstamp: Unknown

No.	Description	Colourways	Size	U.S.$	Can.$	U.K.£
1.	Decanter	Tan/cream, multi coloured print, lettering "Gleneagles Hotel"	250	Unknown		

Hand Bell New Year Gala Banquet and Ball, 1989

This decanter was produced to celebrate the New Year Gala Banquet and Ball held on 10th January 1989.

Photograph not available
at press time

Backstamp: Printed "New Year Gala Banquet and Ball 10th January 1989 Presented by Arthur Bell Distilleries"

No.	Description	Colourways	Size	U.S.$	Can.$	U.K.£
1.	Decanter	Tan/ream; gold crest; red script "Arthur Bell & Sons PLC"	250	Unknown		

Hand Bell 25 Anniversary of Opening of Broxburn 1968 - 1993

Photograph not available
at press time

Backstamp: Printed "25 Anniversary of Opening of Broxburn 1968 - 1993"

No.	Description	Colourways	Size	U.S.$	Can.$	U.K.£
1.	Decanter	White; multi coloured & gold crest; red script "Arthur Bell & Sons"	200	Unknown		

Hand Bell A Memento of Your Visit to Bell's Head Office

Photograph not available
at press time

Backstamp: Unknown

No.	Description	Colourways	Size	U.S.$	Can.$	U.K.£
	Decanter	Tan/cream; black, red and gold label "A Memento of Your Visit to Bell's Head office"	6 2/3rd fluid oz	Unknown		

Hand Bell Miniature To Commemorate a Visit to Scotland, 1986

Photograph not available
at press time

No.	Description	Colourways	Size	U.S.$	Can.$	U.K.£
1.	Decanter	White; red, black/gold label; black lettering "To Commemorate a Visit to Scotland 1986"	Miniature 103	Unknown		

Hand Bell Miniature Cherrybank Gardens, 1991

This miniature decanter with backstamp A is dated 1991 on the back.

Backstamp: A. Purple printed "Genuine Wade Porcelain" and gold printed "Arthur Bell & Son Cherrybank, Perth Scotland"
B. Printed red script "Arthur Bell & Sons" with gold crest

No.	Description	Colourways	Size	U.S.$	Can.$	U.K.£
1.	Decanter	White; gold bands "Bell's Cherrybank Gardens"	98	75.00	90.00	40.00
2.	Decanter	White; gold bands "Bell's Cherrybank Gardens"	98	75.00	90.00	40.00

EXPORT DECANTERS

In 1992 a series of Bell's Christmas decanters was issued for the export market. They are green and cream and are decorated with transfer prints relating to sportsmanship, framed by a red and green holly wreath. The export decanters have been found in Canada, Majorca, South Africa and Spain.

Christmas 1994

Christmas 1995

Backstamp: "Genuine Wade Porcelain"

No.	Description	Colourways	Size	U.S.$	Can.$	U.K.£
1.	Christmas 1988	"We Wish You a Merry Christmas"	200	150.00	200.00	100.00
2.	Christmas 1989	"Perth Scotland Winter 1895"	200	30.00	40.00	20.00
3.	Christmas 1990	"The Art of Distilling Brewery Print"	200	30.00	40.00	20.00
4.	Christmas 1991	"The Art of Distilling Pot Still Print"	200	30.00	40.00	20.00
5.	Christmas 1992	"The Tradition of Curling"	200	75.00	100.00	50.00
6.	Christmas 1993	"The Royal and Ancient Sport of Golf"	200	60.00	80.00	40.00
7.	Christmas 1994	"The Art of Salmon Fishing"	200	60.00	80.00	40.00
8.	Christmas 1995	"The Tradition of Highland Games"	200	60.00	80.00	40.00
9.	Christmas 1996	"The Tradition of Piping"	200	45.00	60.00	30.00
10.	Christmas 1997	"The Fine Art of Stalking"	200	45.00	60.00	30.00
11.	Christmas 1998	"Rainbow Trout Fishing"	75 cl/200	45.00	60.00	30.00

Church Bell Decanter, Hawaii, 12-Year-Old Whisky, 1992 - 1998

The 12-year old whisky decanter has a recessed shield in the centre of the top shoulder.

Photograph not available
at press time

Backstamp: A. "Genuine Wade Porcelain"
B. Printed "Genuine Wade Porcelain"
C. Printed "Wade England" between two lines

No.	Description	Colourways	Size	U.S.$	Can.$	U.K.£
1.	Decanter	White; gold cap, bands; red/white/blue Hawaii flag; gold lettering "Bell's Hawaii"	200	100.00	135.00	55.00
2.	Decanter	Pale blue; gold cap, bands; red/white/blue Hawaii flag; gold lettering "Bell's Hawaii"	200	100.00	135.00	55.00

Church Bell Decanter, South Africa, 1988-1996

Since 1988 Wade has produced decanters for export to South Africa. They contained Bell's Extra Special and 12-year-old Blend. No. 1 and No. 2 were produced from 1988 to 1991; No. 3 and 4 were produced from 1992 to 1996.

Photograph not available
at press time

Backstamp: "Genuine Wade Porcelain"

No.	Description	Colourways	Size	U.S.$	Can.$	U.K.£
1.	12-Year-Old Blend	Green/cream	200	30.00	35.00	15.00
2.	Extra Special	Green/cream	200	30.00	35.00	15.00
3.	12-Year-Old Blend	Green	200	30.00	35.00	15.00
4.	Extra Special	Green	200	30.00	35.00	15.00

Church Bell Decanter, 20-Year-Old Royal Reserve, 1994

Backstamp: None

No.	Description	Colourways	Size	U.S.$	Can.$	U.K.£
1.	Decanter	Blue bottle; white embossed lettering "Royal Reserve Years 20 Old"	210	40.00	45.00	20.00

Church Bell Decanter, Joyous Wedding 12-Year-Old Scotch Whisky, 1988 and 1992

This brightly decorated decanter, which contained 12-year-old blended whisky, has the same print of a bridal couple on it that was used on the "Hand Bell Wedding Day Decanter" of the early 1980s., see page 30. The 1992 decanter has no whisky age.

Photograph not available
at press time

Backstamp: A. "Wade Porcelain Decanter from Bell's Scotch Whisky Perth Scotland, 75cl Product of Scotland 40% vol"
B. "Gold crest, red script Arthur Bell & Sons"

No.	Description	Colourways	Size	U.S.$	Can.$	U.K.£
1.	Decanter 1988	Gold cap; white bottle; multi-coloured print	200	95.00	125.00	60.00
2.	Decanter 1992	Gold cap; white bottle, multi-coloured print black lettering "To Celebrate a Joyous Wedding Day"	200	95.00	125.00	60.00

Hand-Bell Decanters, 1965-1988

From 1965 to the late 1970s, the caps on the bells were ceramic; at some time in the late 1970s, they were replaced by plastic ones. The wording on the gold whisky labels varied over the years, as the metric system of weights and measures was introduced. For Bell's commemorative decanters, see Commemorative section in *The Charlton Standard Catalogue of Wade Vol. 1: General Issues.*

Hand-Bell Decanter, 750 ml, 375 ml, 125 ml, 50 ml

Backstamp: A. "Wade Bell's Scotch Whisky, Perth Scotland"
B. "Wade"

No.	Description	Colourways	Size	U.S.$	Can.$	U.K.£
1.	Decanter	Brown ceramic cap; red-brown/honey bottle	26 fl. oz./250	31.00	38.00	17.00
2.	Decanter	Brown plastic cap; red-brown/honey bottle	750 ml/250	20.00	33.00	12.00
3.	Decanter	Brown ceramic cap; red-brown/honey bottle	13 fl. oz./200	25.00	35.00	12.00
4.	Decanter	Brown plastic cap; red-brown/honey bottle	375 ml/200	20.00	30.00	10.00
5.	Decanter	Brown ceramic cap; red-brown/honey bottle	6 2/3 fl. oz./160	20.00	25.00	10.00
6.	Decanter	Brown plastic cap; red-brown/honey bottle	125 ml/160	15.00	22.00	6.00

Miniature Hand-Bell Decanters, 1979-Date Unknown

Backstamp: "Wade Bell's Scotch Whisky, Perth Scotland

No.	Item	Colourways	Size	U.S.$	Can.$	U.K.£
1.	Decanter	Brown ceramic cap; red-brown/honey bottle;	50 ml/103	22.00	35.00	15.00
2.	Decanter	Brown plastic cap; red-brown/honey bottle;	50 ml/103	20.00	30.00	12.00

Hand Bell, Joyous Wedding Decanter, c.1980

The design for this hand bell is the same as on the 1988 church-bell decanter.

Backstamp: "Wade Porcelain Decanter from Bell's Scotch Whisky Perth Scotland, 75cl Product of Scotland 40% vol"

No.	Description	Colourways	Size	U.S.$	Can.$	U.K.£
1.	Decanter	Gold cap; white bottle; multi-coloured bridal print "To Celebrate a Joyous Wedding Day"	250	60.00	80.00	30.00
2.	Decanter	White cap; white bottle; multi-coloured print	250	95.00	125.00	50.00

DRINK POURERS, c.1965-1995

These drink pourers are circular with straight bases except for No.9 and can be found with either metal or plastic tubes. The shape number, with the above noted exception, is 52A.

Backstamp: A. "Wade Regicor Made in UK " on neck
B. Impressed "C52A" under porcelain button, not seen unless pourer is taken apart

No.	Description	Colourways	Size	U.S.$	Can.$	U.K.£
1.	Drink Pourer	White; metal tube, spout; red/black lettering "Bell's Scotch Afore Ye Go"	41 x 44	25.00	30.00	12.00
2.	Drink Pourer	White; metal tube, spout; dark blue lettering "Bell's Scotch"	41 x 44	25.00	30.00	12.00
3.	Drink Pourer	White; metal tube, spout; red/black lettering "Bell's Scotch Whisky Afore Ye Go"	41 x 44	25.00	30.00	12.00
4.	Drink Pourer	White; metal tube, spout; red lettering "Bell's Scotch"	41 x 44	25.00	30.00	12.00
5.	Drink Pourer	Yellow; plastic tube; brown/red lettering "Bell's Extra Special"	41 x 44	25.00	30.00	12.00

Drink Pourer (No.6)

Drink Pourer (No.7)

Drink Pourer (No.8)

Drink Pourer (No.9)

No.	Description	Colourways	Size	U.S.$	Can.$	U.K.£
6.	Drink Pourer	Yellow; metal spout, neck; brown and cream lettering "Bell's Old Scotch Whisky Extra Special Established 1825"	C53/41 x 44 Round	25.00	30.00	12.00
7.	Drink Pourer	White; metal spout, neck; red/black lettering "Bell's Scotch Whisky Afore ye go"	C53 / 41 x 44 Round	25.00	30.00	12.00
8.	Drink Pourer	Yellow/red band; metal spout, neck; brown/yellow lettering "Bell's Extra Special," crest	C53/41 x 44 Round	25.00	30.00	12.00
9.	Drink Pourer	White/red; metal spout, neck; white lettering "James Bell & Co Special Scotch Whiskey"	C52A/40 x 48 Octagonal	25.00	30.00	12.00

WATER JUGS, 1968-1996

Bell's Old Scotch Whisky (No.1)

Arthur Bell & Sons Ltd (No.2)

Bell's Aged 8 Years (No.3)

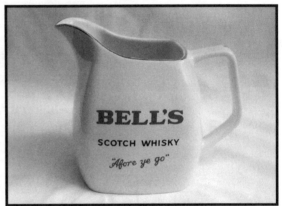

Bell's Scotch Whisky (No.4)

Backstamp: **A.** "Reginald Corfield Limited Redhill Surrey," " Wade Regicor England"
B. "Wade p d m England"
C. Printed circular "Reginald Corfield Limited, Redhill Surrey, " with "Regicor Wade England" through the circle (1968-1969)

No.	Description	Colourways	Shape/Size	U.S.$	Can.$	U.K.£
1.	Ice-check spout	Cream; brown/red crest, lettering "Bell's Old Scotch Whisky"	Round/205	15.00	20.00	8.00
2.	Ice-check spout	White; sepia/brown print; brown lettering "Arthur Bell & Sons Ltd Distillers Perth Scotland Estd. 1825"	Square/127	35.00	40.00	18.00
3.	Open spout	Yellow; brown lettering "Bell's Aged 8 Years"	Round/158	35.00	40.00	18.00
4.	Open spout	White; red/black lettering "Bell's Scotch Whisky 'Afore ye go'"	Square/127	30.00	35.00	15.00

BELTANE SCOTCH WHISKY

DRINK POURER

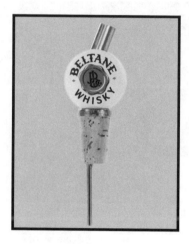

Backstamp: None

No.	Description	Colourways	Size	U.S.$	Can.$	U.K.£
1.	Drink Pourer	White/red seal; metal spout, neck; black lettering "Beltane Whiskey"	Round C53/41 x 44	30.00	25.00	12.00

BERTOLA SHERRY

ASHTRAY

This ashtray is shaped as a sherry bottle.

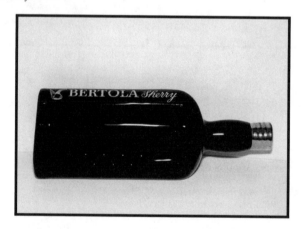

Backstamp: Printed "Wade Regicor London England," laurel leaf frame (large size 18 x 20mm 1953-1962)

No.	Description	Colourways	Size	U.S.$	Can.$	U.K.£
1.	Ashtray	Black; gold rim; white lettering "Bertola Sherry"	215	25.00	35.00	15.00

DECANTER, 1968-1969

This unusual shaped decanter of Spanish origin is used for sangria, a Spanish drink of wine, fruit juice, and/or soda water.

Backstamp: Printed circular "Reginald Corfield Limited, Redhill Surrey, with Regicor Wade England" through the circle (1968-1969)

No.	Description	Colourways	Size	U.S.$	Can.$	U.K.£
1.	Decanter	Black gold crest; white lettering "Bertola Cream Sherry"	229	35.00	45.00	25.00

HORS D'OEUVRES DISH

This unusual shaped dish has a container on the stem for toothpicks.

Backstamp: Transfer print "Wade pdm England" (pdm joined 1969-1984)

No.	Description	Colourways	Size	U.S.$	Can.$	U.K.£
1.	Dish	White; black print; chrome stem "Bertola Cream Sherry"	200	35.00	45.00	20.00

BIG BEN SCOTCH WHISKY

WATER JUG, 1969-1984

Backstamp: "Wade pdm England"

No.	Description	Colourways	Size	U.S.$	Can.$	U.K.£
1.	Open spout	Black; gold print, lettering, "Big Ben Very Old Scotch Whisky"	120	30.00	35.00	18.00

BLACK & WHITE SCOTCH WHISKY
JAMES BUCHANAN & CO LTD.

ASHTRAYS, c.1969-1990

Backstamp: A. "Wade pdm England"
B. "Reginald Corfield Limited Redhill Surrey," "Wade Regicor England"
C. Transfer print "Wade pdm England" (pdm separate 1984-1990)

No.	Description	Colourways	Shape/Size	U.S.$	Can.$	U.K.£
1.	Ashtray	Black; white lettering, "Black & White Scotch Whisky"	Round/127	10.00	15.00	5.00
2.	Ashtray	White; black lettering, "Black & White Scotch Whisky"	Square/127	15.00	20.00	8.00
3.	Ashtray	White; black lettering, "Black & White Scotch Whisky"	Round/127	10.00	15.00	5.00

DECANTER, 1986-1988

The black-and-white "Scottish Terriers Whisky Decanter," which was made for export only, is considered one of Wade's most attractive. There is no Wade backstamp on the decanter; the only reference to Wade is on a gold-and-black oval leaflet which hangs from the neck of one of the dogs. Part of the inscription on the leaflet reads, "This gift decanter has been specially commissioned by James Buchanan and Co. Ltd. from George Wade and Son Ltd."

Backstamp: "Scotch Black & White Whisky Premium, Distilled, Blended and Bottled in Scotland by James Buchanan and Co. Ltd."

No.	Description	Colourways	Size	U.S.$	Can.$	U.K.£
1.	Decanter	White dog; pink mouth, dark brown eyes; grey nose Black dog; brown eyes	200	200.00	275.00	95.00

DRINK POURERS, c.1968

The circular drink pourers have straight bases and are shape number C53. The octagonal pourers are shape number 5455/1, and the rectangular pourer is shape C62.

Backstamp: "Wade Regicor Made in UK" on neck

No.	Description	Colourways	Shape/Size	U.S.$	Can.$	U.K.£
1.	Drink Pourer	White; metal tube, spout; black/white dogs, lettering "Black & White Scotch Whisky"	Circular/41	30.00	35.00	15.00
2.	Drink Pourer	White; metal tube, spout; black/white lettering "Black & White Scotch Whisky"	Circular/41	30.00	35.00	15.00
3.	Drink Pourer	White/black; plastic tube; thin white lettering "Black & White Scotch Whisky"	Octagonal/40	30.00	35.00	15.00
4.	Drink Pourer	White/black; plastic tube; thick white lettering "Black & White Scotch Whisky"	Octagonal/40	30.00	35.00	15.00
5.	Drink Pourer	Black; metal spout, neck; white panel with dogs; black lettering "Black & White Scotch Whisky"	C62/47 x 41 Rectangular	30.00	35.00	15.00

WATER JUGS, 1969-1984

Black & White Scotch Whisky (No.1)

Black & White the Scotch With Character (No.3)

Black & White Scotch Whisky Buchanan's
(No.4)

Backstamp: **A.** "Reginald Corfield Limited Redhill Surrey," "Wade Regicor England"
B. "Wade pdm England"
C. Transfer printed "Made In Great Britain Wade Regicor"
D. Transfer printed "Wade pdm England" (pdm joined 1969-1984)

No.	Description	Colourways	Shape/Size	U.S.$	Can.$	U.K.£
1.	Ice-check spout	Black; gold rim; black/white print; white lettering "Black & White Scotch Whisky"	Round/155	35.00	40.00	18.00
2.	Open spout	Black; white lettering "Black & White Scotch Whisky Buchanan's"	Round/127	35.00	40.00	18.00
3.	Ice-check spout	Black; black/white dogs print; white lettering "Black & White The Scotch With Character"	Round/175	35.00	40.00	18.00
4.	Open spout	Black; white circle/lettering "Black & White Scotch Whisky Buchanan's"	Round/155	35.00	40.00	18.00

BLACK BOTTLE SCOTCH WHISKY
GORDON GRAHAM

ASHTRAY AND WATER JUGS, 1984-1990

Water jug No. 2 has an ice-check spout and is decorated with a print of a bottle. No. 3 has an open spout.

Ashtray   Water Jug, open spout (No. #)

Backstamp: "Wade p d m England"

No.	Description	Colourways	Shape/Size	U.S.$	Can.$	U.K.£
1.	Ashtray	Black; black/white lettering "Black Bottle Scotch Whisky" Gordon Graham facsimile signature	Square/133	10.00	15.00	5.00
2.	Water Jug, ice-check spout	Black; white print, lettering "Black Bottle Scotch Whisky"	Rectangular/140	25.00	30.00	12.00
3.	Water Jug, open spout	Black; gold/white lettering "Black Bottle Scotch Whisky"	Rectangular/140	15.00	20.00	8.00
4.	Water Jug, open spout	Black; white circle lettering "Black & White Scotch Whisky Buchanan's"	Round/155	35.00	40.00	18.00

THE BLACK PRINCE SCOTCH WHISKY

DECANTER, 1997

This beautifully decorated decanter appears to have been made for export as there is a Japanese inscription on the back.

Backstamp: Gold printed "The Black Prince Scotch Whisky Company Limited Genuine Wade Porcelain" with shield

No.	Description	Colourways	Shape/Size	U.S.$	Can.$	U.K.£
1.	Decanter	Marbled blue; multi-coloured print; gold/black lettering "Aged Over 25 Years The Black Prince 1st Son of Edward III Earl of Chester Edward of Woodstock"	Round/195	40.00	50.00	25.00

BLACKTHORN CIDER

ASHTRAY AND BAR SNACK DISH

Ashtray

Bar Snack Dish

Backstamp: Transfer print "Wade pdm England" (pdm joined 1969-1984)

No.	Description	Colourways	Shape/Size	U.S.$	Can.$	U.K.£
1.	Ashtray	Cream; black line, lettering "Blackthorn Cider"	Round/125	12.00	18.00	8.00
2.	Snack Dish	Cream; black line, lettering "Blackthorn Cider Cooled On Draught "	Round/185	12.00	18.00	8.00

BLACK VELVET RYE

DRINK POURERS, c.1980

The Wade shape number for the octagonal drink pourer is 5455/1. The square pourer has a notched base and shoulders and came equipped with a plastic tube. It is Wade shape number C52A.

Photograph not available
at press time

Backstamp: Unmarked

No.	Description	Colourways	Shape/Size	U.S.$	Can.$	U.K.£
1.	Drink Pourer	Black; gold lettering "Black Velvet Rye"	Octagonal/40	30.00	35.00	15.00
2.	Drink Pourer	Black; gold lettering "Black Velvet Rye"	Square/38	30.00	35.00	15.00

BOMBAY DRY GIN
BOMBAY SPIRITS COMPANY

ASHTRAY, ICE BUCKET AND WATER JUGS, 1969-1990

The ashtray was produced between 1969 and 1984, the ice bucket in 1971 and the water jug between 1984 and 1990.

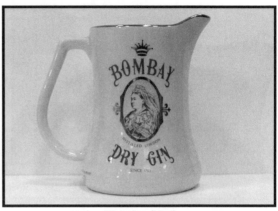

Ashtray (No.1)   Water Jug (No.4)

Backstamp: **A.** "Wade pdm England"
B. "Wade p d m England"
C. Printed "Fine Staffordshire Pottery Duncan & Fox Co. Inc. New York Regicor Wade Made in England"
D. Printed "Wade Regicor Made in England"

No.	Description	Colourways	Shape/Size	U.S.$	Can.$	U.K.£
1.	Ashtray	White; black print, lettering "Bombay London Dry Gin"	Round/153	20.00	30.00	12.00
2.	Ice Bucket/ lid	White; green/gold print, lettering "Bombay Gin"	165	70.00	90.00	45.00
3.	Water Jug	White; black print, lettering "Bombay London Dry Gin"	Round/165	15.00	20.00	8.00
4.	Water Jug	Cream; green/gold print; green lettering "Bombay distilled London Dry Gin since 1761"	Round/153	45.00	55.00	25.00
5.	Water Jug	Cream; green/gold print; green lettering "Bombay Dry Gin"	Round/65 Miniature	25.00	35.00	15.00

DRINK POURERS

Drink Pourer (No.1)

Drink Pourer (No.2)

Backstamp: Impressed "C52A" under porcelain button, not seen unless pourer is taken apart

No.	Description	Colourways	Shape/Size	U.S.$	Can.$	U.K.£
1.	Drink Pourer	White; plastic spout/neck; green lettering "Bombay London Dry Gin"	C52A/40 x 48	25.00	30.00	12.00
2.	Drink Pourer	Black; metal spout, neck; white gem; gold lettering "Bombay Sapphire"	C62/47 x 41 Rectangular	25.00	30.00	10.00
3.	Drink Pourer	Black; metal spout, neck; white lettering "Bombay Sapphire"	C62/47 x 41 Rectangular	25.00	30.00	10.00

BOOTH'S GIN

ASHTRAYS, 1955-1984

"Booth's & Orange" (No. 1)

Backstamp: **A.** "Wade Regicor, London England," laurel leaves, large size
B. "Reginald Corfield Limited Redhill Surrey," "Wade Regicor England"
C. "Wade pdm England"

No.	Description	Colourways	Shape/Size	U.S.$	Can.$	U.K.£
1.	Ashtray	White/orange; red print; black lettering "Booth's & Orange"	Round/140	10.00	15.00	5.00
2.	Ashtray	White/black; red print; white lettering "Booth's Gin"	Round/146	10.00	15.00	5.00
3.	Ashtray	White; blue disc; red lion; white lettering "Booth's Gins"	Round/164	10.00	15.00	5.00
4.	Ashtray	Black; red print, white lettering "Booth's Ltd"	Square/140	15.00	20.00	8.00
5.	Ashtray	Black; red print, white lettering "Booth's Gins"	Square/159	15.00	20.00	8.00

DRINK POURERS

Drink Pourer (No.1)

Drink Pourer (No.2)

Drink Pourer (No.3)

Backstamp: Impressed "5455/1" on underside of button

No.	Description	Colourways	Shape/Size	U.S.$	Can.$	U.K.£
1.	Drink Pourer	White; metal spout, tube; red Lion print; black upper case lettering "Booth's Gin"	Round C53/41 x 44	25.00	30.00	10.00
2.	Drink Pourer	White/yellow; metal spout, tube; red Lion print; black lettering "Booth's Gin"	Round C53/41 x 44	25.00	30.00	10.00
3.	Drink Pourer	White; plastic spout, tube; red Lion print; black lettering "Booth's Gin"	Octagonal 5455/140 x 47	25.00	30.00	10.00

BORZOI VODKA
JAMES BURROUGH LTD.

ASHTRAYS AND WATER JUGS, 1968-1984

The ashtrays were produced between 1968 and 1969, and the water jugs between 1969 and 1984. The jugs have an ice-check spout and a print on it of the vodka label.

Ashtray (No.1)

Ashtray (No.2)

Water Jug (No.4)

Water Jug (No.5)

Backstamp: **A.** "Reginald Corfield Limited Redhill Surrey," "Wade Regicor England"
B. Printed circular "Reginald Corfield Limited, Redhill Surrey, " with "Regicor Wade England" through the circle (1968-1969)

No.	Description	Colourways	Shape/Size	U.S.$	Can.$	U.K.£
1.	Ashtray	White; red/black/white lettering "Borzoi Vodka"	Square/153	15.00	20.00	8.00
2.	Ashtray	White; white/red/black lettering "Borzoi Vodka Purity with a Pedigree "	Square/140	12.00	18.00	8.00
3.	Water Jug	White; multi-coloured print	Rectangular/159	35.00	40.00	18.00
4.	Water Jug	White; red/orange label white/black lettering "Borzoi Dry Imperial Vodka Imported"	Triangular/159	35.00	40.00	18.00
5.	Water Jug	White; red label; white/red/black lettering "Produced & Bottled in England Borzoi Dry Imperial Vodka Distilled & Bottled by James Burrough Ltd"	Triangular /159	35.00	40.00	18.00

BOWMORE MALT WHISKY

ASHTRAY, 1969-1984

Backstamp: "Wade pdm England"

No.	Description	Colourways	Shape/Size	U.S.$	Can.$	U.K.£
1.	Ashtray	Dark brown; gold print/lettering "Bowmore Pure Malt Whisky"	Round/146	15.00	20.00	8.00

BRAKSPEAR'S HENLEY ALES

WATER JUG, 1968-1969

Backstamp: "Reginald Corfield Limited Redhill Surrey," "Wade Regicor England"

No.	Description	Colourways	Shape/Size	U.S.$	Can.$	U.K.£
1.	Water Jug, open spout	White; red/black print; black lettering "Brakspear's Henley Ales"	Rectangular/145	35.00	40.00	20.00

BREAKER REAL MALT LIQUOR

ASHTRAY, 1969-1984

Backstamp: "Wade pdm England"

No.	Description	Colourways	Shape/Size	U.S.$	Can.$	U.K.£
1.	Ashtray	Peach; blue and white print; white lettering "Breaker Real Malt Liquor"	Round/205	10.00	15.00	5.00

BRONTE LIQUEUR

LIQUEUR JUGS, 1991-1993

The Bronte Liqueur Company was formed by the descendants of the famous literary sisters Emily and Charlotte Bronte. Jugs No. 3 and 4 have a cameo portrait of Emily Bronte as part of the label, while jug No. 5 has an embossed portrait of her on the front of the jug.

Produced in three sizes, 24 oz., 12 oz., and miniature. The miniature was first produced in a two-tone glaze of amber brown and cream. A second version is all brown, a slightly smaller size, and the shape has also altered.

Amber jug with spout (No. 3)   Amber jug with spout (No. 4)   Amber jug with spout (No. 5)

Backstamp: A. Raised "Created for the James B Beam Import Corp by Bronte Liqueur Co. Ltd"
B. Embossed "Created for the James Beam Import Corp by Bronte Liqueur York Yorkshire England Made by Wade Ireland"
C. Unmarked

No.	Name	Colourways	Shape/Size	U.S.$	Can.$	U.K.£
1.	Jug, 1 oz.	Brown/cream	Miniature/76	15.00	18.00	15.00
2.	Jug, 1 oz.	Honey brown	Miniature/74	15.00	18.00	15.00
3.	Jug 12 oz, with spout.	Amber/cream	3/4 pint/150	25.00	35.00	18.00
4.	Jug, 12 oz, without spout.	Amber/cream	3/4 pint/175	25.00	35.00	18.00
5.	Jug, 12 oz, with spout.	White/amber; embossed cameo	35 cl/175	70.00	85.00	40.00
6.	Jug, 20 oz, without spout	Amber/cream	Pint/205	30.00	45.00	22.00

BUCHANAN'S SCOTCH WHISKY

ASHTRAYS AND WATER JUGS, 1968-1990

The No. 1 ashtray was produced between 1968 and 1969, the No.3 jug between 1969 and 1984, and No. 4 and 5 between 1969 and 1990. The No. 3 jug has an ice-check spout and no handle; No. 4 and 5 have an open spout. The print on No. 5 is a portrait of a man.

Ashtray (No.1)

Ashtray (No.2)

"Buchanan's de luxe Scotch Whisky" Jug (No.3)

Backstamp: **A.** "Reginald Corfield Limited Redhill Surrey," "Wade Regicor England"
B. "Wade pdm England"
C. "Wade p d m England"

No.	Description	Colourways	Shape/Size	U.S.$	Can.$	U.K.£
1.	Ashtray	Royal blue; gold lettering "Buchanan's De Luxe Scotch Whisky"	Square/205	12.00	15.00	8.00
2.	Ashtray	Royal blue; gold/red lettering "Buchanan's De Luxe 12 Years Old Scotch Whisky"	Round/185	8.00	12.00	5.00
3.	Water Jug	Royal blue; gold lettering "Buchanan's De Luxe Scotch Whisky"	Round/177	25.00	30.00	12.00
4.	Water Jug	Yellow; black lettering "Buchanan's Scotch"	Round/155	25.00	30.00	12.00
4.	Water Jug	White; multi-coloured print; black lettering "The Buchanan's The Scotch of a Lifetime"	Round/153	30.00	35.00	15.00

BULMERS CIDER

ADVERTISING DISPLAY POMONA, 1982

Less than 100 of this unusual bar top display model was produced for Bulmers Cider in 1982. The model is in two pieces: the round indented base holds four bottles of Bulmers No. 7 Extra Dry Still Cider, and the centre piece is a model of Pomona, goddess of the orchards, who is holding a large basket of apples.

Backstamp: Printed circular "Wade pdm" (pdm joined 1969-1984)

No.	Description	Colourways	Shape/Size	U.S.$	Can.$	U.K.£
1.	Advertising Display	White; black lettering "Bulmers No 7 "	229 x 254		Very Rare	

ASHTRAY, 1969-1984

The print on this ashtray contains a woodpecker.

Backstamp: "Wade pdm England"

No.	Description	Colourways	Shape/Size	U.S.$	Can.$	U.K.£
1.	Ashtray	Yellow; multi-coloured print; red/white lettering "Bulmers Woodpecker Cider"	Oval/171	10.00	15.00	5.00

BURNETT'S WHITE SATIN DRY GIN

ASHTRAY

Backstamp: White printed "Wade Regicor London England" (large size 18 x 20 mm 1953-1962)

No.	Description	Colourways	Shape/Size	U.S.$	Can.$	U.K.£
1.	Ashtray	Dark green; white lettering "Burnett's White Satin Dry London Gin"	Round/140	12.00	15.00	8.00

DRINK POURER

Photograph not available
at press time

No.	Description	Colourways	Shape/Size	U.S.$	Can.$	U.K.£
1.	Drink Pourer	Black; metal spout, neck; white lettering "White Satin Burnett's Dry Gin"	Round C53/41 x 44	25.00	30.00	15.00

BUSHMILLS IRISH WHISKEY

DECANTER

This decanter/whiskey jug is similar in shape to the Irish Wade Poteen Jug. It has a two tone glaze, the top half is green and the bottom half off-white, and there is a print of a pair of pheasants on the front.

Photograph not available
at press time

Backstamp: Printed "Wade Ireland"

No.	Description	Colourways	Shape/Size	U.S.$	Can.$	U.K.£
1.	Decanter/ whisky jug	Flying Pheasants, green/off white jug; multi-coloured print	140	25.00	40.00	20.00

DRINK POURER

No.	Description	Colourways	Shape/Size	U.S.$	Can.$	U.K.£
1.	Drink Pourer	Black/gold; metal spout, neck white lettering "Bushmills Malt Aged 10 Years"	Round C53/41 x 44	25.00	35.00	12.00

WATER JUGS, 1984-1990

These jugs have an ice-check spout.

Backstamp: A. "Wade p d m England"
B. Printed in oval "Irish Distillers The Spirit of Ireland"

No.	Description	Colourways	Shape/Size	U.S.$	Can.$	U.K.£
1.	Water Jug	Black; gold/black/red label, lettering, "Special Old Irish Whiskey Black Bush"	Rectangular/133	35.00	40.00	18.00
2.	Water Jug	Black; multi coloured label, print white/gold lettering "Special Old Irish Whiskey Black Bush…"	Rectangular/165	35.00	40.00	18.00

CAIN'S BEER

ASHTRAY, 1993-1996

The print on this ashtray is of a building.

Photograph not available
at press time

Backstamp: "Wade P D M Made in England"

No.	Description	Colourways	Shape/Size	U.S.$	Can.$	U.K.£
1.	Ashtray	Yellow; gold/black print; red/gold/black lettering "Cain's Traditional English Beer"	Arch/171	15.00	20.00	8.00

CAMPARI ORANGE BITTERS

DRINK POURER

Backstamp: Impressed "C52A" under porcelain button, not seen unless pourer is taken apart

No.	Description	Colourways	Shape/Size	U.S.$	Can.$	U.K.£
1.	Drink Pourer	White/blue; plastic spout, neck; white lettering "Campari"	C52A/40 x 48 Octagonal	25.00	30.00	10.00

CAMUS COGNAC

DRINK POURER

Backstamp: None

No.	Description	Colourways	Shape/Size	U.S.$	Can.$	U.K.£
1.	Drink Pourer	Black; metal spout, neck; gold lettering "Camus Cognac" and crest	Round C53/41 x 44	30.00	35.00	12.00

CANADIAN CLUB WHISKY

ASHTRAY AND WATER JUGS, c.1953-1984

The round water jug has an open spout, but the oval and square-shaped jugs have ice check spouts.

Water Jug (No.3)	Water Jug (No.4)	Water Jug (No.5)

Backstamp: **A.** "Wade p d m England"
B. "Reginald Corfield Limited Redhill Surrey," "Wade Regicor England'
C. Printed "Wade Regicor England," in a laurel leaf frame (large size 18 x 20 mm 1953-1962)
D. Printed circular "Reginald Corfield Limited, Redhill Surrey," with "Regicor Wade England" through the circle (1968-1969) "86.8 Proof Blended Canadian Whisky Imported By Bottle By Hiram Walker Importers INC. Detroit Mich"

No.	Description	Colourways	Shape/Size	U.S.$	Can.$	U.K.£
1.	Ashtray	White; red/black lettering "Canadian Club"	101	15.00	20.00	8.00
2.	Water Jug	White; black lettering "Canadian Club"	Oval/171	30.00	35.00	15.00
3.	Water Jug	White; gold lettering "Canadian Club C.C. The Best In The House"	Oval/165	35.00	50.00	25.00
4.	Water Jug	White; red flag; black lettering "Canadian Club"	Square/140	30.00	35.00	18.00
5.	Water Jug	White; red wreath/lettering "Canadian Club Whisky"	Round/110	30.00	35.00	18.00

DRINK POURERS

Drink Pourer (No.1)   Drink Pourer (No.2)

No.	Description	Colourways	Shape/Size	U.S.$	Can.$	U.K.£
1.	Drink Pourer	White; all porcelain; black lettering "Canadian Club"	AP3/130	25.00	30.00	15.00
2.	Drink Pourer	Black; metal spout, neck; white lettering "Canadian Club"	Round C53/41 x 44	25.00	30.00	12.00

CAPTAIN MORGAN RUM

ASHTRAYS AND DRINK POURERS, c.1958-1962

The ashtrays were produced between 1960 and 1962, and the drink pourer circa 1958 to circa 1962. The drink pourer is all porcelain and has a round base. These items are decorated with a print of Captain Morgan.

Rowboat Ashtray (No.2)

Drink Pourer (No.3)

Drink Pourer (No.4)

Drink Pourer (No.5)

Backstamp: **A.** "Wade Regicor, London England," laurel leaves, large size
B. "Wade Regicor Made in UK"
C. Printed "Wade Regicor Made in England," in laurel leaf frame (small size 13 x 13 mm 1962-late 1968)

No.	Description	Colourways	Shape/Size	U.S.$	Can.$	U.K.£
1.	Ashtray	Black/white boat; multi-coloured print; black/white lettering on stern, sides and inside boat "Captain Morgan Rum"	Boat/235	42.00	58.00	26.00
2.	Ashtray	Black/white boat; multi-coloured print; black/white lettering inside boat "Captain Morgan Rum"	Boat/235	42.00	58.00	26.00
3.	Drink Pourer	White; porcelain spout, tube; multi-coloured print	Circular/41	30.00	35.00	15.00
4.	Drink Pourer	White; all porcelain red lettering (front) "Captain Morgan Rum;" portrait (Back)	AP2/117	25.00	30.00	15.00
5.	Drink Pourer	White; all porcelain red lettering (front) "Captain Morgan Rum;" portrait (back)	AP3/130	25.00	30.00	15.00

CARLING BLACK LABEL

ASHTRAYS, 1968-1990

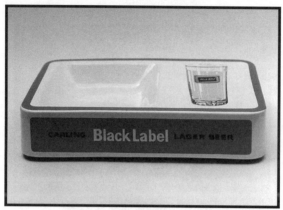

Ashtray (No.2)

Backstamp: A. "Reginald Corfield Limited Redhill Surrey,'" "Wade Regicor England"
B. "Wade pdm England"
C. "Wade p d m England"

No.	Description	Colourways	Shape/Size	U.S.$	Can.$	U.K.£
1.	Ashtray	Black/gold; red/white/black lettering "Carling Black Label Lager Beer"	Rectangular/210	15.00	20.00	8.00
2.	Ashtray	White/red; yellow/black pint print; black/white lettering "Carling Black Label Lager Beer"	Rectangular/252	8.00	10.00	5.00
3.	Ashtray	Black; red/white/black lettering "Black Label"	Square/140	10.00	15.00	5.00

MENU HOLDER

Backstamp: Printed "Wade Regicor Made in U.K." (c.late 1960s)

No.	Description	Colourways	Shape/Size	U.S.$	Can.$	U.K.£
1.	Menu Holder	White/black/red; red/white print, lettering "Carling Black Label Lager Beer"	Square/55	18.00	25.00	12.00

WATER JUGS, 1969-1990

Photograph not
available
at press time

No.	Description	Colourways	Shape/Size	U.S.$	Can.$	U.K.£
1.	Water Jug, ice-check spout	Black; red/white/gold lettering "Carling Black Label Lager"	Triangular/165	28.00	40.00	22.00
2.	Water Jug, open spout	White; black/red/white "Carling Black Label Lager"	Triangular/165	28.00	40.00	22.00

CARLSBERG

ASHTRAYS, 1935-1937, 1969-1984

Ashtray No. 1 is the oldest piece of Wade Liquor Advertising found to date, it has the 1935-1937 backstamp and is decorated in a Flaxman Ware glaze. The central design is of an embossed crown in a star and it has embossed lettering around the rim.

Ashtray (No.1)   Carlsberg Lager Pilsner (No. 2)

Backstamp: A. "Wade pdm England"
B. Transfer print "Wade pdm England" (pdm joined 1969-1984)

No.	Description	Colourways	Shape/Size	U.S.$	Can.$	U.K.£
1.	Ashtray	Sea green/brown; embossed off-white lettering, "Carlsberg Lager Pilsner"	Round/133	60.00	70.00	35.00
2.	Ashtray	White; black print; red lettering "Carlsberg" "Copenhagen"	Square/140	15.00	20.00	8.00
3.	Ashtray	White; black lettering "Carlsberg Export HOF"	Square/140	15.00	20.00	8.00

CASTAWAY WINE COOLER

WATER JUG

Backstamp: Printed "Wade pdm Made in England" within two red lines, one thick, the other thin (1990-1996)

No.	Description	Colourways	Shape/Size	U.S.$	Can.$	U.K.£
1.	Water Jug	Creamy yellow; green/black palm trees print, black/green/red lettering "Castaway Wine Cooler Sparkling Drink with White Wine and The Juice of Tropical Fruits Containing 50% White Wine-Serve Cool"	Round/172	25.00	35.00	15.00

CATTO'S SCOTCH WHISKY

ASHTRAY AND WATER JUGS, 1955-1990

The larger round jug has an ice-check spout and the smaller one an open spout and a recessed handle.

Ashtray (No.1)

Water Jug (No.3)

Backstamp: **A.** "Wade Regicor, London England," laurel leaves, large size
B. "Wade p d m England"
C. Printed "Wade pdm Made in England" within two red lines; one thick, the other thin (1990-1996)

No.	Description	Colourways	Shape/Size	U.S.$	Can.$	U.K.£
1.	Ashtray	Black; gold lettering "Catto's Scotch Whisky"	Square/171	10.00	15.00	5.00
2.	Water Jug	Black; gold lettering "Catto's Scotch Whisky"	Round/165	25.00	30.00	12.00
3.	Water Jug	Black; gold lettering "Catto's Scotch Whisky"	Round/127	30.00	40.00	15.00

CHAMPION MARLI BITTERS FINLAND

DRINK POURER

No.	Description	Colourways	Shape/Size	U.S.$	Can.$	U.K.£
1.	Drink Pourer	White; metal spout, neck red lettering "Champion Marli"	Round C53/41 x 44	25.00	30.00	12.00

CHARLES KINLOCH WINE SELLERS

DRINK POURERS

Drink Pourer (No.1)   Drink Pourer (No.2)

Backstamp: Impressed "5455/1" on underside of button

No.	Description	Colourways	Shape/Size	U.S.$	Can.$	U.K.£
1.	Drink Pourer	White/green; metal spout, neck lettering "Selected By Charles Kinloch"	5455/140 x 47 Octagonal	25.00	30.00	10.00
2.	Drink Pourer	White/blue; plastic spout, neck white lettering "Selected By Charles Kinloch"	5455/140 x 47 Octagonal	25.00	30.00	10.00

CHARRINGTON

ASHTRAYS, 1969-1990

Oval Ashtray (No.1)

Backstamp: **A.** "Wade Regicor, London England," Hand Painted
B. "Wade pdm England"
C. "Wade p d m England"
D. Printed "Wade Regicor London England," in laurel leaf frame

No.	Description	Colourways	Shape/Size	U.S.$	Can.$	U.K.£
1.	Ashtray	Mottled grey; green/yellow print; yellow lettering "Charrington Established 1757"	Oval/216	20.00	30.00	10.00
2.	Ashtray	Cream; black lettering "Charrington IP"	Square/140	10.00	15.00	5.00
3.	Ashtray	Dark green; black/orange/green Toby print gold/black lettering "Charrington Best Toby Ale"	Square/190	10.00	15.00	6.00

MATCHBOOK HOLDER

Backstamp: Printed "Wade - Regicor London England," laurel leaf frame

No.	Description	Colourways	Size	U.S.$	Can.$	U.K.£
1.	Matchbook Holder	White; black print; white/red lettering "The Best Beers in Britain Come from Charrington"	50 Rectangular	12.00	18.00	8.00

Backstamp: Printed "Wade Regicor London England," laurel leaf frame (large size 18 x 20 mm 1953-1962)

No.	Description	Colourways	Size	U.S.$	Can.$	U.K.£
1.	Tankard	White; gold bands; multi-coloured print of Toby Philpot	Traditional/Pint 125	12.00	18.00	8.00

TOBY JUGS, 1958

"Charrington" (No.1)

"Toby Ale" (No.2)

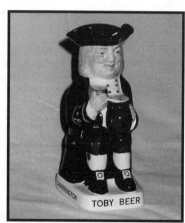

"Toby Jug" (No.3)

Backstamp: "Wade Regicor, London England, Hand Painted"

No.	Description	Colourways	Size	U.S.$	Can.$	U.K.£
1.	Charrington	Maroon trousers; dark green coat; lettering "Charrington"	180	165.00	230.00	95.00
2.	Toby Ale	Maroon trousers; dark green coat; lettering "Toby Ale"	180	165.00	230.00	95.00
3.	Toby Beer	Maroon trousers; dark green coat black lettering "Toby Beer"	190	165.00	230.00	95.00

Derivative

LAMP, c.1958-1984

Advertising lamps were not sold to the public but were commissioned by breweries to advertise and decorate the public houses and hotel bars that sold their beers. This Charrington Toby Ale Lamp is from the same mould as that used for the toby jugs. A hole was drilled in the base for the wiring, and lamp fittings were added. The lettering is around the sides of the base. This lamp was originally produced c.1958, then reissued between 1969 and 1984.

Photograph not available
at press time

Backstamp: A. "Wade Regicor, London England, Hand Painted"
B. "Wade pdm England"

No.	Description	Colourways	Size	U.S.$	Can.$	U.K.£
1.	Lamp	Maroon trousers; dark green coat "Toby Ale"	180	125.00	155.00	65.00

CHEQUERS SCOTCH WHISKY

DRINK POURER AND WATER JUG, 1969-1984

The jug has an ice-check spout.

Drink Pourer

Water Jug

Backstamp: A. "Wade pdm England"
B. Transfer printed "Wade pdm England" (joined 1969-1984) and "Chequers Blended Scotch Whiskey 86.8 Proof Custom Import House Ltd. New York"

No.	Description	Colourways	Shape/Size	U.S.$	Can.$	U.K.£
1.	Drink Pourer	Black metal spout, neck; white lettering "Superb Chequers Blended Scotch Whisky"	C53/41 x 44 Round	25.00	30.00	12.00
2.	Water Jug	Green; white lettering "Chequers Scotch Whisky"	Round/153	35.00	45.00	22.00

CHIVAS BROTHERS LIMITED

ASHTRAY, 1984-1995

Photograph not available at press time

Backstamp: "Wade P D M England"

No.	Description	Colourways	Shape/Size	U.S.$	Can.$	U.K.£
1.	Ashtray	Black; white lettering "Chivas Scotch"	Round/140	15.00	20.00	8.00

DECANTERS

Celebration 25yrs

Photograph not available at press time

Backstamp: Unknown

No.	Description	Colourways	Size	U.S.$	Can.$	U.K.£
1.	Bottle	White; gold cap, labels; red/black/gold lettering "Celebration 25yrs"	750/215	30.00	40.00	15.00

The Directors Celebration Reserve

Photograph not available at press time

Backstamp: Unknown

No.	Description	Colourways	Size	U.S.$	Can.$	U.K.£
1.	Decanter	Black; gold cap, labels, lettering "The Directors Celebration Reserve"	750/215	30.00	40.00	15.00

DRINK POURER

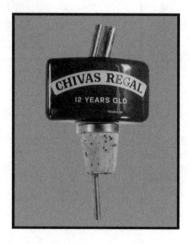

Backstamp: Unknown

No.	Description	Colourways	Size	U.S.$	Can.$	U.K.£
1.	Drink Pourer	Red; metal spout, neck; red/white lettering "Chivas Regal 12 Years Old"	Rectangular C54/37 x 60	25.00	30.00	15.00

HIP FLASKS, 1974-1995

These flat-sided flasks were issued between 1974 and 1995.

Photograph not available
at press time

Backstamp: A. "Chivas Brothers Limited, Aberdeen Scotland, Wade England, Liquor Bottle"
B. "Wade p d m England"

No.	Description	Colourways	Size	U.S.$	Can.$	U.K.£
1.	Hip Flask	Brown	200 ml/153	25.00	30.00	12.00
2.	Hip Flask	Indigo blue	200 ml/153	25.00	30.00	12.00
3.	Hip Flask	Light green	200 ml/153	25.00	30.00	12.00
4.	Hip Flask	Pink	200 ml/153	25.00	30.00	12.00
5.	Hip Flask	Sea green	200 ml/153	25.00	30.00	12.00

ROYAL SALUTE WHISKY BOTTLES, 1974-1996

Whisky Bottle

Boxed Miniature Whisky Bottles

Backstamp: "Chivas Brothers Limited, Aberdeen Scotland, Wade England, Liquor Bottle"

No.	Description	Colourways	Size	U.S.$	Can.$	U.K.£
1.	Whisky Bottle	Brown; gold labels	750 ml/215	30.00	38.00	15.00
2.	Whisky Bottle	Indigo blue; gold labels	750 ml/215	30.00	38.00	15.00
3.	Whisky Bottle	Light green; gold labels	750 ml/215	30.00	38.00	15.00
4.	Whisky Bottle	Pink; gold labels	750 ml/215	30.00	38.00	15.00
5.	Whisky Bottle	Sea green; gold labels	750 ml/215	30.00	38.00	15.00
6.	Whisky Bottle	Brown; gold labels	375 ml/185	20.00	25.00	12.00
7.	Whisky Bottle	Indigo blue; gold labels	375 ml/185	20.00	25.00	12.00
8.	Whisky Bottle	Light green; gold labels	375 ml/185	20.00	25.00	12.00
9.	Whisky Bottle	Pink; gold labels	375 ml/185	20.00	25.00	12.00
10.	Whisky Bottle	Sea green; gold labels	375 ml/185	20.00	25.00	12.00
11	Whisky Bottle	Brown; gold labels	200 ml/153	15.00	20.00	10.00
12	Whisky Bottle	Indigo blue; gold labels	200 ml/153	15.00	20.00	10.00
13	Whisky Bottle	Light green; gold labels	200 ml/153	15.00	20.00	10.00
14	Whisky Bottle	Pink; gold labels	200 ml/153	15.00	20.00	10.00
15.	Whisky Bottle	Sea green	200 ml/153	15.00	20.00	10.00
16.	Whisky Bottle	Indigo blue; gold labels	50 ml/101	22.00	30.00	12.00
17.	Whisky Bottle	Pink; gold labels	50 ml/101	22.00	30.00	12.00
18.	Whisky Bottle	Sea green; gold labels	50 ml/101	22.00	30.00	12.00

WATER JUGS, 1984-1996

Backstamp: Printed circular "Wade pdm England" (pdm separated 1984-1990)

No.	Description	Colourways	Size	U.S.$	Can.$	U.K.£
1.	Water Jug, open spout	Cream; maroon bands; gold lettering "Chivas Regal 12 Year Old Scotch Whisky"	Round/130	30.00	35.00	12.00
2.	Water Jug, open spout	Maroon; gold lettering "Chivas Regal 12 yr old Whisky"	205	25.00	30.00	12.00

CINZANO

ASHTRAY, 1969-1984

Photograph not available
at press time

Backstamp: "Wade pdm England"

No.	Description	Colourways	Shape/Size	U.S.$	Can.$	U.K.£
1.	Ashtray	White; black lettering "Cinzano Secco"	Square/140	10.00	15.00	5.00

CLUNY SCOTCH WHISKY
MACPHERSON'S

ASHTRAYS, 1955-1969

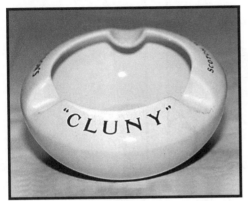

Round Astray (No.1)

Square Astray (No.2)

Backstamp: A. "Wade Regicor, London England," laurel leaves, large size
B. "Reginald Corfield Limited Redhill Surrey," "Wade Regicor England"

No.	Description	Colourways	Shape/Size	U.S.$	Can.$	U.K.£
1.	Ashtray	White; red/black lettering "Cluny Scotch Whisky"	Round/159	15.00	20.00	8.00
2.	Ashtray	Black; gold lettering "Cluny Scotch Whisky"	Square/114	15.00	20.00	8.00

DRINK POURERS

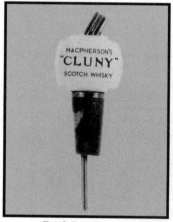

Drink Pourer (No.1)

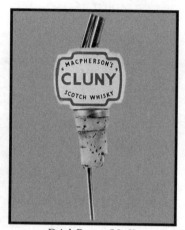

Drink Pourer (No.2)

Drink Pourer (No.3)

Backstamp: A. Impressed "C52A" under porcelain button, not seen unless pourer is taken apart

No.	Description	Colourways	Shape/Size	U.S.$	Can.$	U.K.£
1.	Drink Pourer	White; metal spout, tube blue lettering "Machperson's Cluny Scotch Whisky"	C52A/40 Octagonal	25.00	30.00	12.00
2.	Drink Pourer	White; metal spout, tube; black/red lettering "Machperson's Cluny Scotch Whisky"	C52A/40 x 48 Octagonal	25.00	30.00	12.00
3.	Drink Pourer	White/yellow; red band; metal spout, black/red lettering "Macpherson's Cluny Scotch Whisky"	C52A/40 x 48 Octagonal	25.00	30.00	12.00

COOPE IND HOTELS

ASHTRAY

Backstamp: Green printed "Wade pdm" (pdm joined 1969-1984)

No.	Description	Colourways	Shape/Size	U.S.$	Can.$	U.K.£
1.	Ashtray	Cream, blue print; white lettering "Coope Ind Hotels"	Round/114	12.00	15.00	6.00

CORK DRY GIN

DRINK POURER

Backstamp: Impressed "C52A" under porcelain button, not seen unless pourer is taken apart

No.	Description	Colourways	Shape/Size	U.S.$	Can.$	U.K.£
1.	Drink Pourer	White/red; metal spout, neck white lettering "Cork Dry Gin"	C52A/40 x 48 Octagonal	30.00	35.00	12.00

COSSACK VODKA

DRINK POURERS

Drink Pourer (No.1)   Drink Pourer (No.2)

Backstamp: Impressed "5455/1" on underside of button

No.	Description	Colourways	Shape/Size	U.S.$	Can.$	U.K.£
1.	Drink Pourer	White; metal spout, neck black/ red lettering "Cossack Vodka"	C53/41 x 44 Round	25.00	30.00	15.00
2.	Drink Pourer	White; plastic spout, neck black/red lettering "Cossack Vodka"	5455/140 x 47 Octagonal	25.00	30.00	15.00

WATER JUG, *1984-1990*

This water jug has an ice-check spout and no handle.

Photograph not available
at press time

Backstamp: "Wade p d m England"

No.	Description	Colourways	Shape/Size	U.S.$	Can.$	U.K.£
1.	Water Jug	Royal blue; white lettering "Cossack Vodka"	Round /177	30.00	35.00	18.00

COURVOISIER COGNAC

ASHTRAYS, *1969-1984*

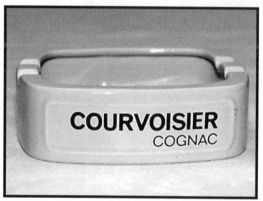 

Ashtray (No.1)   Ashtray (No.2)

Backstamp: A. "Wade pdm England"
B. "Wade pdm England" (pdm joined 1969-1984)

No.	Description	Colourways	Shape/Size	U.S.$	Can.$	U.K.£
1.	Ashtray	Grey; red lettering "Courvoisier Cognac"	Rectangular /147	10.00	15.00	5.00
2.	Ashtray	Grey; red Napoleon print, lettering "Courvoisier Cognac"	Circular /190	10.00	12.00	6.00

DRINK POURERS, 1969-1984

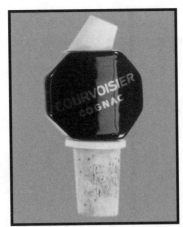

Drink Pourer (No.1)

Backstamp: Impressed "5455/1" on underside of button

No.	Description	Colourways	Shape/Size	U.S.$	Can.$	U.K.£
1.	Drink Pourer	Black; plastic tube; gold lettering "Courvoisier Cognac"	5455-1/Octag./40	30.00	35.00	15.00
2.	Drink Pourer	Black; plastic spout, neck; gold lettering "Courvoisier Cognac"	5455-1/Octag./40 x 47	25.00	30.00	12.00

CRAWFORD'S SCOTCH WHISKY

DRINK POURERS

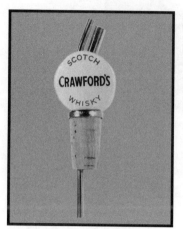

Drink Pourer (No.1)   Drink Pourer (No.2)

Backstamp: Printed "Wade Regicor Made in England," in laurel leaf frame

No.	Description	Colourways	Shape/Size	U.S.$	Can.$	U.K.£
1.	Drink Pourer	White; metal spout, neck, black/red lettering "Crawford's Scotch Whisky"	C53/41 x 44 Round	30.00	38.00	12.00
2.	Drink Pourer	White; all porcelain; black/red lettering "Scotch Crawford's Whisky"	AP3/130	25.00	30.00	15.00

WATER JUGS, 1953-1984

The spouts on these jugs are open. The first two jugs have been found in two sizes: the normal pint size and a much rarer miniature size.

Round Jug "Old Scotch Crawford's Whisky"

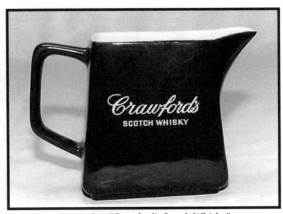

Square Jug "Crawford's Scotch Whisky"

Backstamp: **A.** "Wade Regicor, London England," laurel leaves, large size
B. "Wade pdm England"
C. Printed "Wade Regicor Made in England," in laurel leaf frame

No.	Description	Colourways	Shape/Size	U.S.$	Can.$	U.K. £
1.	Water Jug	Salmon pink; red/black lettering "Old Scotch Crawford's Whisky"	Miniature/75 mm	38.00	50.00	15.00
2.	Water Jug	Salmon pink; red/black lettering "Old Scotch Crawford's Whisky"	Round/102	38.00	50.00	15.00
3.	Water Jug	Maroon; white lettering "Crawford's Scotch Whisky"	Square/101	25.00	30.00	12.00

CREAM OF THE BARLEY
STEWART'S DUNDEE

ASHTRAYS, 1953-1962

Ashtray (No.2)

Backstamp: "Wade Regicor, London England," laurel leaves, large size

No.	Description	Colourways	Shape/Size	U.S.$	Can.$	U.K.£
1.	Ashtray	White; honey print; black/red lettering "Cream of the Barley Quality Scotch"	Square/133	15.00	20.00	8.00
2.	Ashtray	Orange/red; black lettering "Stewart's Dundee De Luxe Scotch Whisky Cream of the Barley"	Square/60 x 115	10.00	12.00	6.00

DRINK POURERS

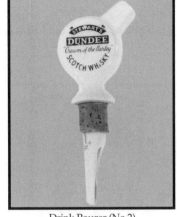

Drink Pourer (No.1)   Drink Pourer (No.2)

Backstamp: A. Printed "Wade - Regicor London England," laurel leaf frame (1953-1962)
B. Impressed "C52A" under porcelain button, not seen unless pourer is taken apart

No.	Description	Colourways	Shape/Size	U.S.$	Can.$	U.K.£
1.	Drink Pourer	White; metal spout, neck blue lettering, "Stewart's Dundee Cream of the Barley Scotch Whisky"	C52A/40 Octagonal	30.00	38.00	12.00
2.	Drink Pourer	White; all porcelain white/black lettering, "Stewart's Dundee Cream of the Barley Scotch Whisky"	AP3/130	25.00	30.00	15.00

CROFT WHISKY

DRINK POURER

This pourer, shape number 52A, is square with a notched base and shoulders.

Photograph not available
at press time

Backstamp: Unmarked

No.	Description	Colourways	Shape/Size	U.S.$	Can.$	U.K.£
1.	Drink Pourer	Black; plastic tube; gold/white lettering "Croft Original"	Square/38	30.00	35.00	15.00

CUTTY SARK SCOTCH WHISKY
BERRY BROS. & RUDD LTD.

ASHTRAY AND WATER JUGS, 1968-1990

The ashtray was produced between 1968 and 1969. The water jugs between 1969 and 1990. The round jug has an ice-check spout and is decorated with a print of the bottle label. Jug No. 3 has an open spout and no handle. The print on it depicts a sailing ship. The last two jugs, both large and small versions, have recessed handles and ice-check spouts.

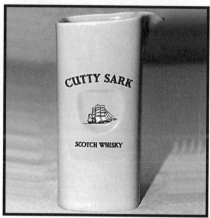

Water Jug "Bottle Label" (No.2)   Water Jug "Scotch Whisky" (No3)

Backstamp: **A.** "Reginald Corfield Limited Redhill Surrey," "Wade Regicor England"
B. "Wade p d m England"
C. "Wade pdm England Imported by the Buckingham Corporation New York NY. Distilled Blended and Bottled in Scotland 86 proof"

No.	Description	Colourways	Shape/Size	U.S.$	Can.$	U.K.£
1.	Ashtray	Black; yellow lettering "Cutty Sark Scotch Whisky"	Round/127	10.00	15.00	5.00
2.	Water Jug	Dark green; yellow bottle label print; black lettering "Cutty Sark"	Round/165	20.00	30.00	10.00
3.	Water Jug	Yellow; white print; black lettering "Cutty Sark Scotch Whisky"	Rectangular/170	40.00	45.00	20.00
4.	Water Jug	Black; yellow print, lettering "Cutty Sark Scotch Whisky"	Large Round/177	25.00	35.00	18.00
5.	Water Jug	Black; yellow print, lettering "Cutty Sark Scotch Whisky"	Small Round/114	20.00	30.00	15.00

DRINK POURERS

Drink Pourer (No.1)   Drink Pourer (No.2)

Backstamp: None

No.	Description	Colourways	Shape/Size	U.S.$	Can.$	U.K.£
1.	Drink Pourer	White/yellow; metal spout, neck; black lettering "Cutty Sark"	C53/41 x 44 Round	25.00	30.00	12.00
2.	Drink Pourer	White/yellow; plastic spout, neck; black lettering "Cutty Sark"	C53A/41 x 44 Oval	25.00	30.00	12.00

DANDIE DINMONT SCOTCH WHISKY

WATER JUG

This water jug has an ice-check spout and a print of the Dandie Dinmont terrier dog on the front.

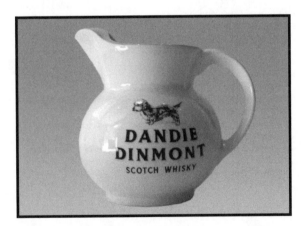

Backstamp: Printed "86.8 Proof Scotch Whisky Imported by Vintage Wines, Inc; New York, N.Y. Wade England"

No.	Description	Colourways	Shape/Size	U.S.$	Can.$	U.K.£
1.	Water Jug	White; black print, lettering "Dandie Dinmont Scotch Whisky"	140	40.00	50.00	20.00

DEWAR'S SCOTCH WHISKY
UNITED DISTILLERS UK PLC

ASHTRAYS, 1953-1990

The ashtrays were produced between 1953 and 1990.

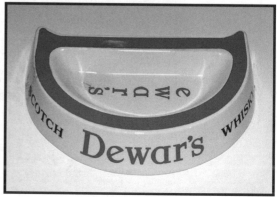

Oval Ashtray "Dewar's Special Scotch Whisky" (No. 2)   D-shaped Ashtray "Dewar's Scotch Whisky" (No. 8)

Backstamp: **A.** "Wade Regicor, London England," laurel leaves, large size
B. "Wade Regicor, London England," laurel leaves, small size
C. "Wade pdm England" (pdm joined 1969-1984)
D. "Wade p d m England"
E. "Wade Regicor Made in UK" on neck

No.	Description	Colourways	Shape/Size	U.S.$	Can.$	U.K.£
1.	Ashtray	White; red/black lettering "Dewar's"	D-shaped/190	30.00	35.00	15.00
2.	Ashtray	Yellow; red/black lettering "Dewar's Special Scotch Whisky"	Oval/152	10.00	15.00	5.00
3.	Ashtray	Yellow; red/black lettering "Dewar's Scotch Whisky"	Oval/165	10.00	15.00	5.00
4.	Ashtray	White; red/black lettering "Dewar's White Label"	Round/120	15.00	20.00	8.00
5.	Ashtray	Yellow; red/black lettering "Dewar's White Label"	Round/120	15.00	20.00	8.00
6.	Ashtray	Black; maroon/white lettering "Dewar's De Luxe Ancestor Scotch Whisky"	Square/101	25.00	30.00	12.00
7.	Ashtray	Black/maroon; white lettering "Dewar's De Luxe Ancestor Scotch Whisky"	Square/140	10.00	15.00	5.00
8.	Ashtray	White; red rim; red/black lettering "Dewar's Scotch Whisky"	D-shaped/184	25.00	35.00	18.00
9.	Ashtray	Dark green; maroon/gold label; gold lettering "Dewar's aged 12 years Ancestor Scotch Whisky"	Rectangular/260	12.00	15.00	8.00

DRINK POURERS

The drink pourers were issued circa 1960. The circular pourers, shape number C53, have a straight base. Style No. 1 is an older pourer, with a flap on the top of the metal spout to prevent dust getting in.

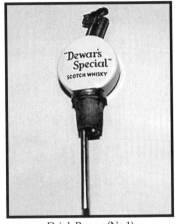
Drink Pourer (No.1)

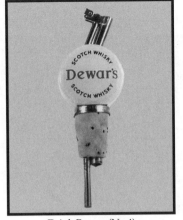
Drink Pourer (No.4)

Drink Pourer (No.5)

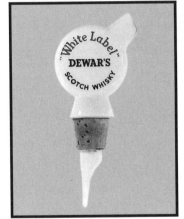
Drink Pourer (No.6)

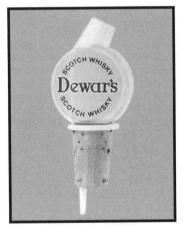
Drink Pourer (No.7)

Backstamp: No backstamp

No.	Description	Colourways	Shape/Size	U.S.$	Can.$	U.K.£
1.	Drink Pourer	White/yellow; metal tube, spout, flap; red/ black lettering "Dewar's Special Scotch Whisky"	C53/41 Round	30.00	35.00	15.00
2.	Drink Pourer	White; plastic tube; black/red lettering "Dewar's White Label"	C53/41 Round	30.00	35.00	15.00
3.	Drink Pourer	White; metal tube, spout; red/black lettering lettering "White Label Dewar's"	C53/41 Round	30.00	35.00	15.00
4.	Drink Pourer	White/yellow; metal spout, neck with dust flap; red/black lettering "Scotch Whisky Dewar's Scotch Whisky"	C53/41 x 44 Round	30.00	35.00	15.00
5.	Drink Pourer	White/yellow; metal spout, neck with dust flap; black/red lettering "White Label Dewar's Scotch Whisky"	C53/41 x 44 Round	30.00	35.00	15.00
6.	Drink Pourer	White; all porcelain; red/black lettering "White Label Dewar's Scotch Whisky"	AP4/117 Round	25.00	30.00	15.00
7.	Drink Pourer	White/yellow; plastic spout, neck; black/red lettering "White Label Dewar's Scotch Whisky"	C53A/40 x 44 Round	25.00	30.00	12.00

WATER JUGS, 1953-1990

These jugs all have ice-check spouts and are decorated with a print of the Dewar's Highlander. Style No. 4 has a recessed handle.

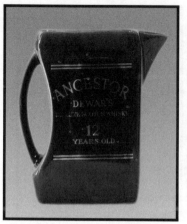

Rectangular Jug, recess handle (No.6)

Round Jug, short spout (No.7)

Round Jug, short spout (No.9)

Backstamp:
A. "Wade Regicor, London England," laurel leaves, large size
B. "Reginald Corfield Limited Redhill Surrey," "Wade Regicor England"
C. Transfer print "Wade pdm England" (pdm joined 1969-1984)
D. Circular transfer printed "Reginald Corfield Ltd Redhill Surrey-Wade Regicor England" (late 1968-late 1969)

No.	Description	Colourways	Shape/Size	U.S.$	Can.$	U.K.£
1.	Flat Sides	Yellow; red/black print, lettering "Dewar's Fine Scotch Whisky"	Round/146	25.00	30.00	12.00
2.	Long Spout	White; black print, black/red lettering "Dewar's White Label Scotch Whisky"	Round/153	25.00	30.00	12.00
3.	Long Spout	Yellow; black print, black/red lettering "Dewar's is the Scotch"	Round/165	25.00	30.00	12.00
4.	Long Spout	Yellow; black/red print, lettering "White Label Dewar's Scotch Whisky"	Round/165	25.00	30.00	12.00
4.	Long Spout	Yellow jug; black Highlander print; black/red lettering "Dewar's Special Scotch Whisky"	165mm	26.00	36.00	12.00
6.	Recess Handle	Black; gold lettering "Ancestor Dewar's De Luxe Scotch Whisky 12 Years Old"	Rectangular/146	30.00	35.00	12.00
7.	Short Spout	Yellow; black print, lettering "Dewar's Special Scotch Whisky"	Round/159	30.00	35.00	15.00
8.	Short Spout	Yellow jug; black/red lettering "White Label Dewar's Scotch Whisky"	159 mm	26.00	36.00	12.00
9.	Short Spout	White jug; black Highlander print black lettering "Dewar's White Label Scotch Whisky"	153mm	26.00	36.00	12.00

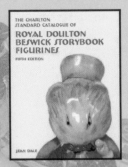

DIMPLE SCOTCH WHISKY

ASHTRAY, 1994-1996

Backstamp: "Wade P D M Made in England"

No.	Description	Colourways	Shape/Size	U.S.$	Can.$	U.K.£
1.	Ashtray	Maroon; gold crest, lettering "The Original Dimple"	Triangular/177	10.00	15.00	5.00

DECANTERS

Souvenir Decanters, 1984-1990

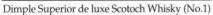

Dimple Superior de luxe Scotoch Whisky (No.1)　　　　Dimple Decanter (No.2)

Backstamp: "John Haig & Co Ltd. Edinburgh, Scotland"

No.	Description	Colourways	Size	U.S.$	Can.$	U.K.£
1.	Superior de luxe Scotch Whisky	White; gold laurel leaves; multi-coloured print, lettering "Dimple Superior De Luxe"	215	40.00	45.00	20.00
2.	Superior de luxe	Black; gold laurel leaves; crest and lettering	216	35.00	45.00	20.00
3.	Dimple Export, Hawaii	White; gold laurel leaves; multi-coloured print	216	40.00	45.00	20.00
4.	Dimple Export, Hong Kong	Unknown	216	40.00	45.00	20.00

1984 Los Angeles

1985 Tsukuba

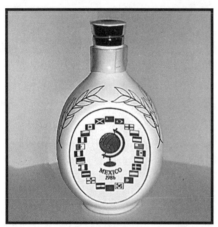

1986 Mexico

1986 Scotland

Backstamp: "John Haig & Co. Ltd 75cl 43GL Markinch Scotland"

No.	Description	Colourways	Size	U.S.$	Can.$	U.K.£
1.	1984 Los Angeles	White/gold laurel leaves; blue/red wreath "In Commemoration of the Summer Games Los Angeles 1984"	216	40.00	45.00	20.00
2.	1985 Tsukuba	White/gold laurel leaves; blue/yellow birds "In Commemoration of Tsukuba Expo 85"	216	40.00	45.00	20.00
3.	1986 Mexico	White/gold laurel leaves; flags of the world "Mexico 1986"	216	40.00	45.00	20.00
4.	1986 Scotland	White/gold laurel leaves; emblems of Scotland and the "Games XIII Commonwealth Games Scotland 1986"	216	40.00	45.00	20.00

Chinese New Year Decanters, 1986-1992

These decanters are decorated with prints of the animals that represent each year.

1989 Year of the Snake

1989 Year of the House

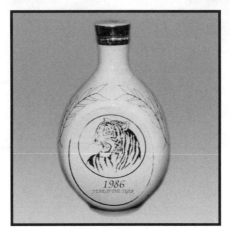

1986 Year of the Tiger

Backstamp: Circular gold print "John Haig 75cl 43 GL Edinburgh Scotland"

No.	Description	Colourways	Size	U.S.$	Can.$	U.K.£
1.	1986 Year of the Tiger	White; black print; red lettering	216	40.00	50.00	25.00
2.	1987 Year of the Rabbit	Unknown colours	216	40.00	50.00	20.00
3.	1988 Year of the Dragon	Black; Gold print & lettering	216	40.00	50.00	25.00
4.	1989 Year of the Snake	White; gold print and lettering	216	40.00	50.00	25.00
5.	1990 Year of the Horse	Black; gold print and lettering	216	40.00	50.00	25.00
6.	1991 Year of the Sheep	Unknown	216	40.00	50.00	25.00
7.	1992 Year of the Monkey	Unknown	216	40.00	50.00	25.00

DRINK POURER, 1990-1995

This drink pourer, shape C53, has a straight base.

Photograph not available
at press time

No.	Description	Colourways	Shape/Size	U.S.$	Can.$	U.K.£
1.	Drink Pourer	White/red; black lettering "Haig"	Circular/41	30.00	35.00	15.00

DOMECQ SHERRY

ASHTRAYS

This rectangular ashtray with an arched centre has a blue-grey print of the Domecq winery. The "Celebration Cream" ashtray is dated 1962-1968.

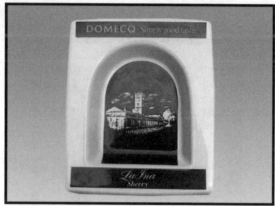

Ashtray "Domecq Simply Goodtaste La Ina Sherry" (No.1)

Backstamp: A. Printed "Wade pdm Made in England" (pdm joined 1969-1984)
                B. "Wade Regicor, London England," laurel leaves, small size

No.	Description	Colourways	Shape/Size	U.S.$	Can.$	U.K.£
1.	Ashtray	White; blue grey print; yellow/white lettering on black/blue bands "Domecq Simply Goodtaste La Ina Sherry"	Rectangular/170	12.00	18.00	8.00
2.	Ashtray	White; gold.black logo; black lettering "Celebration Cream Sherry by Domecq"	Round/120	15.00	20.00	8.00

DRINK POURERS

Drink Pourer (No.1)

Drink Pourer (No.2)

Drink Pourer (No.3)

Backstamp: Impressed 5455/1" on underside of button

No.	Description	Colourways	Shape/Size	U.S.$	Can.$	U.K.£
1.	Drink Pourer	White/black panel; plastic spout, neck; yellow/ black lettering "Domecq Double Century Sherry"	40 x 47 Octagonal	25.00	30.00	10.00
2.	Drink Pourer	White/blue panel; plastic spout, neck; white/ blue lettering "Sherry Domecq Sherry"	40 x 47 Octagonal	25.00	30.00	10.00
3.	Drink Pourer	White/black panel, plastic spout, neck; yellow/black lettering "Domecq La Ina Sherry"	5455/1/40 x 47 Octagonal	25.00	30.00	10.00

DON CORTEZ

ASHTRAY, 1968-1969

Backstamp: "Reginald Corfield Limited Redhill Surrey," "Wade Regicor England"

No.	Description	Colourways	Shape/Size	U.S.$	Can.$	U.K.£
1.	Ashtray	White; black/orange lettering "Don Cortez Spanish Wines by Grants of St. James's"	Square/146	15.00	20.00	8.00

DON JON ALE

ASHTRAY, 1955-1962

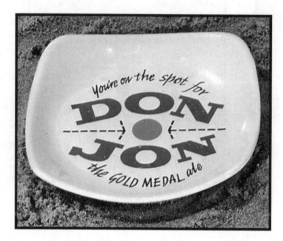

Backstamp: "Wade Regicor, London England," laurel leaves, large size

No.	Description	Colourways	Shape/Size	U.S.$	Can.$	U.K.£
1.	Ashtray	White; yellow print; red/yellow lettering "You're on the Spot for Don Jon the Gold Medal ale"	Square/140	15.00	20.00	8.00

DOUBLE CENTURY SHERRY

ASHTRAY, 1955-1962

Photograph not available
at press time

Backstamp: "Wade Regicor, London England," laurel leaves, large size

No.	Description	Colourways	Shape/Size	U.S.$	Can.$	U.K.£
1.	Ashtray	White; black lettering "Double Century Sherry"	Round/140	15.00	20.00	8.00

DOUBLE DIAMOND

ASHTRAYS, 1968-1990

Ashtray (No.5)

Backstamp: A. "Reginald Corfield Limited Redhill Surrey," "Wade Regicor England"
      B. "Wade p d m England"
      C. Printed "Wade - Regicor London England," in laurel leaf frame (small size 13 x 13mm 1962-late 1968)
      D. Printed circular "Reginald Corfield Limited, Redhill Surrey,"
          with "Regicor Wade England" through the circle (1968-1969)

No.	Description	Colourways	Shape/Size	U.S.$	Can.$	U.K.£
1.	Ashtray	White; green lettering "Double Diamond"	Round/114	15.00	20.00	8.00
2.	Ashtray	Black; multi-coloured label, print "Double Diamond"	Square/101	10.00	15.00	5.00
3.	Ashtray	Black; gold/red and white lettering "Double Diamond Original Burton Ale"	Round/100	12.00	15.00	8.00
4.	Ashtray	Cream; blue/red/orange DD print; white lettering "Double Diamond Works Wonders"	Round/115	12.00	15.00	8.00
5.	Ashtray	White; dark blue centre; red/orange DD print; white lettering "Double Diamond Works Wonders"	Round/115	12.00	15.00	8.00

DRAMBUIE

DRINK POURERS

The No. 1 pourer, shape number C52A, has a notched base and shoulders. Pourer No. 2 is shape C57, which has a rounded top and base and straight sides.

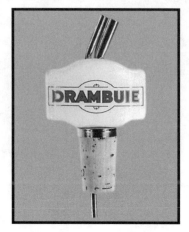

Backstamp: A. Unmarked
            B. Impressed "C57" on underside of button

No.	Description	Colourways	Shape/Size	U.S.$	Can.$	U.K.£
1.	Drink Pourer	White; plastic tube; red lettering "Drambuie"	Square/38	30.00	35.00	15.00
2.	Drink Pourer	White; metal tube; red lettering "Drambuie"	Oval/41	30.00	35.00	15.00
3.	Drink Pourer	White; metal spout, neck; red lettering "Drambuie"	C57/29 x 60 Rectangular	30.00	35.00	12.00

DRYBROUGHS

LOVING CUP, 1981

This loving cup has a print of the brewery with the words "The Location of Drybrough's First Brewery 1750-1981" on the front.

Backstamp: Unknown

No.	Description	Colourways	Shape/Size	U.S.$	Can.$	U.K.£
1.	Loving Cup	Brown; black/brown label, lettering "Dryborough"	Pint/120	50.00	70.00	25.00

DUFF GORDON SHERRY

DRINK POURERS

Drink Pourer (No.1)   Drink Pourer (No.2)

Backstamp: None

No.	Description	Colourways	Shape/Size	U.S.$	Can.$	U.K.£
1.	Drink Pourer	White/red/green metal spout neck/dust cover; white/green /red lettering (front) "Santa Maria Duff Gordon Cream Sherry" (back) "El Cid Duff Gordon Medium Sherry"	C53/41 x 44 Round	25.00	30.00	12.00
2.	Drink Pourer	White/green metal spout, neck/dust cover, white/red lettering (front) "Duff Gordon Santa Maria Cream Sherry" (back) "Duff Gordon El Cid Medium Sherry"	C53/41 x 44 Round	25.00	30.00	12.00

DUNCAN MACGREGOR SCOTCH WHISKY

WATER JUGS, 1969-1984

Backstamp: A. "Wade pdm England" (pdm joined 1969-1984)
B. Printed "Wade pdm England" (pdm joined 1969-1984)

No.	Description	Colourways	Shape/Size	U.S.$	Can.$	U.K.£
1.	Water Jug	Cream; brown lettering "Duncan MacGregor Scotch Whisky"	Triangular/146	25.00	30.00	12.00
2.	Water jug	White; red lettering "Duncan MacGregor Scotch Whisky"	Triangular/146	25.00	35.00	15.00

ETIQUETTE

HIP FLASK, 1997

Backstamp: Gold printed "Genuine Wade England"

No.	Description	Colourways	Shape/Size	U.S.$	Can.$	U.K.£
1.	Golf Ball Hip Flask	White; multi-coloured print "Etiquette Finest Scotch Whisky"	Unknown	45.00	60.00	30.00

THE FAMOUS GROUSE SCOTCH WHISKY
MATTHEW CLOAG & SONS LTD.

ASHTRAYS, 1969-1996

The ashtrays were produced between 1969 and 1996, the decanter from 1993 to 1996, the drink pourers circa 1970, and the water jugs between 1984 and 1996. The octagonal pourer is shape number 5455/1. The square pourers, shape C52A, have a notched base and shoulders. The water jugs have open spouts. All items are decorated with the Grouse Scotch logo.

Ashtray (No.2)

Backstamp: **A.** "Wade pdm England"
B. "Wade P D M England"
C. "Genuine Wade Porcelain"
D. Printed "Wade pdm England" (pdm joined 1969-1984)

No.	Description	Colourways	Shape/Size	U.S.$	Can.$	U.K.£
1.	Ashtray	Yellow; red lettering, "The Famous Grouse"	Round/140	15.00	20.00	5.00
2.	Ashtray	White; brown print; red/black lettering "The Famous Grouse Finest Scotch Whisky"	Round/185	15.00	20.00	5.00
3.	Ashtray	Yellow; black grouse print; black/red lettering "The Famous Grouse Finest Scotch Whisky"	Oval/60 x 140	10.00	12.00	6.00

DECANTER, 1993-1996

Backstamp: Printed "The Famous Grouse Finest Scotch Whiskey Highland Decanter Genuine Wade Porcelain B"

No.	Description	Colourways	Shape/Size	U.S.$	Can.$	U.K.£
1.	Decanter	Pale yellow; multi-coloured print, lettering "Famous Grouse Decanter"	248	45.0	60.00	50.00

DRINK POURERS, c.1970

Drink Pourer (No.1)	Drink Pourer (No.2)	Drink Pourer (No.3)

Backstamp: Impressed "C52A" under porcelain button, not seen unless pourer is taken apart

No.	Description	Colourways	Shape/Size	U.S.$	Can.$	U.K.£
1.	Drink Pourer	White/cream; metal spout, neck; red, black lettering "The Famous Grouse Finest Scotch Whisky"	C52A/40 x 48	25.00	30.00	12.00
2.	Drink Pourer	White; plastic spout, neck; front plain white; back with red/black lettering "The Famous Grouse Finest scotch Whisky "	C52A/40 x 48	25.00	30.00	12.00
3.	Drink Pourer	White/cream; plastic spout, neck; red, black lettering "The Famous Grouse Finest Scotch Whisky" Octag.	C52A/40 x 48	25.00	30.00	12.00
4.	Drink Pourer	Black; plastic spout, neck; gold grouse print; no lettering	C53/41 x 44 Round	25.00	30.00	10.00

WATER JUGS, 1984-1996

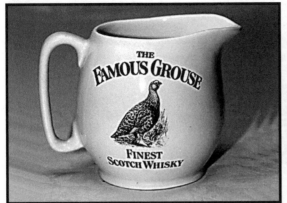

Water Jug (No.2)

Water Jug (No.3)

No.	Description	Colourways	Size	U.S.$	Can.$	U.K.£
1.	Water Jug	White; brown print; red/brown lettering "The Famous Grouse Finest Scotch Whisky"	Round/114	30.00	35.00	15.00
2.	Water Jug	Cream; brown print; red/brown lettering "The Famous Grouse Finest Scotch Whisky"	Round/114	30.00	35.00	15.00
3.	Water Jug	White; grey/brown grouse, red/black lettering; "The Famous Grouse Finest Scotch Whisky" "Product of Scotland"	Round footed/155	35.00	40.00	18.00

FINDLATER'S SCOTCH WHISKY LTD.

DECANTERS, 1986-1990

Football and Rugby Ball Decanter

"1889 Centenary 1989" (No.2)

Backstamp: Black transfer print "Designed for Findlater's Scotch Whisky hand crafted porcelain by Wade Ceramics"

No.	Description	Colourways	Size	U.S.$	Can.$	U.K.£
1.	Football	White/black; black lettering	130	80.00	100.00	45.00
2.	Football	White/black; black lettering "1889 Centenary 1989"	130	80.00	100.00	45.00
3.	Football	White/black; black lettering "World Cup Italy 1990"	130	90.00	135.00	58.00
4.	Rugby Ball	Beige; black lettering	200	95.00	125.00	55.00
5.	Rugby Ball	White; black lettering	200	95.00	125.00	55.00

Royal Prestige Pear-Shaped Decanters

These decanters were sold at the Buffalo I.A.J.B.B.S.C./Wade Show and are also available through the Wade shop. For more information on the The International Association of Jeam Beam Bottle and Specialties Club (IAJBBSC), see page 139.

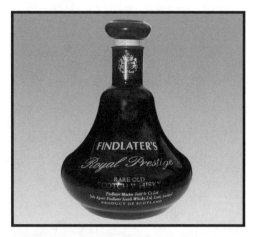

Backstamp: Red printed "Genuine Wade Porcelain"

No.	Description	Colourways	Size	U.S.$	Can.$	U.K.£
1.	Decanter	Dark blue; gold lettering "Findlater's Royal Prestige Rare Old Scotch Whisky"	Large/315	72.00	95.00	45.00
2.	Decanter	Dark blue; gold lettering "Findlater's Royal Prestige Rare Old Scotch Whisky"	Miniature/100	10.00	14.00	5.50

FLOWERS BEER

THE FLOWERS BREWMASTER, c.1958-c.1962

The figure of the Flowers brewmaster served as the logo for the Flowers Brewery before it was taken over by Whitbread, and he served as the model for this figure. This extremely rare piece was produced as an advertising model meant to stand on the bar of a public house.

Backstamp: "Wade Regicor, London England," laurel leaves, large size

No.	Description	Colourways	Size	U.S.$	Can.$	U.K.£
1.	Bar Figure	Red hat, leggings; white shirt, apron; black shoes; gold medallion, red/gold tankard, gold lettering "Brewmaster Brewed by Flowers"	140	290.00	325.00	150.00

FULLER SMITH & TURNER PLC

ASHTRAY AND WATER JUGS, 1984-1995

The spouts on these water jugs are open.

Backstamp: A. "Wade p d m England"
B. "Wade p d m Made in England"

No.	Description	Colourways	Shape/Size	U.S.$	Can.$	U.K.£
1.	Ashtray	Brown; off-white print; embossed lettering "Fuller Smith & Turner P.L.C. Established 1845 Griffin Brewery. Chiswick. Fullers"	Oval/220 x 140	12.00	15.00	10.00
2.	Water Jug	Brown; off-white print; embossed lettering "Fuller Smith & Turner P.L.C. Established 1845 Griffin Brewery Chiswick Fullers"	Rectangular/155	25.00	30.00	12.00
3.	Water Jug	Dark brown; light brown lettering "Fullers-Griffin Brewery Chiswick"	Rectangular/165	25.00	30.00	12.00

GEORGE SANDEMAN AND CO. LTD.

DECANTERS, 1958-1960

The label on the back of the George Sandeman Don Port Bottle reads: "This Don Decanter Contains Partners Port Produce of Portugal Shipped by Sandeman Contents Equal Half Bottle."

Backstamp: Embossed "Wade England," white transfer print "Wade England"

No.	Description	Colourways	Size	U.S.$	Can.$	U.K.£
1.	Sandeman Port	Black; ruby red glass	215	75.00	90.00	32.00
2.	Sandeman Sherry	Black; golden yellow glass	215	85.00	100.00	35.00

GILBEY'S GIN
W & A GILBEY'S WINE SELLERS LIMITED

ASHTRAYS AND DRINK POURERS, 1953-1984

Ashtray "Gilbey's London Dry Gin" (No.1)

Ashtray "Gilbey's" (No.2)

Drink Pourer "GILBEY'S TRIPLE CROWN PORT" (No.5)

Backstamp: **A.** "Wade Regicor, London England," laurel leaves, large size
B. "Wade pdm England" (pdm joined 1969-1984)
C. Printed "Wade pdm England" (pdm joined 1969-1984)
D. Impressed "5455/1" on underside of button

No.	Description	Colourways	Shape/Size	U.S.$	Can.$	U.K.£
1.	Ashtray	Dark green; white lettering "Gilbey's London Dry Gin"	Round/127	15.00	20.00	8.00
2.	Ashtray	Green; white lettering, "Gilbey's"	Round/127	10.00	15.00	5.00
3.	Ashtray	White; black crest/lettering "The Hallmark of Fine Sherry"	Hexagonal/177	20.00	28.00	8.00
4.	Drink Pourer	White/red; metal spout, neck; white lettering "Gilbey's"	Octagonal/40 x 47	25.00	30.00	12.00
5.	Drink Pourer	Black; plastic spout, neck; gold white lettering "Gilbey's Triple Crown Port"	Octagonal/40 x 47	25.00	30.00	12.00

WATER JUG, 1953-1984

Backstamp: White "Wade Regicor Made in England designed for W & A Gilbey Limited by W.M. de Majo FSIA MBE c 1961"

No.	Description	Colourways	Shape/Size	U.S.$	Can.$	U.K.£
1.	Water Jug	Blue; white lettering "Gilbey's Dry Gin"	Round/168	40.00	56.00	28.00

WINE BARRELS, 1958-1961

Backstamp: "Royal Victoria Pottery, Wade England8

No.	Description	Colourways	Size	U.S.$	Can.$	U.K.£
1.	Brandy	White; gold/purple bands; black lettering	½ bottle/115	30.00	38.00	18.00
2.	Cognac	White; gold bands; black lettering	½ bottle/115	30.00	38.00	18.00
3.	Gin	White; gold/blue bands; black lettering	½ bottle/115	30.00	38.00	18.00
4.	Irish	White; gold/yellow bands; black lettering	½ bottle/115	30.00	38.00	18.00
5.	Port	White; gold/maroon bands; black lettering	½ bottle/115	30.00	38.00	18.00
6.	Rye	White; gold/red bands; black lettering	½ bottle/115	30.00	38.00	18.00
7.	Rum	White; gold/orange bands; black lettering	½ bottle/115	30.00	38.00	18.00
8.	Scotch	White; gold/red bands; black lettering	½ bottle/115	30.00	38.00	18.00
9.	Sherry	White; gold/green bands; black lettering	½ bottle/115	30.00	38.00	18.00
10.	Whisky	White; gold/red bands; black lettering	½ bottle/115	30.00	38.00	18.00
11.	Cognac	White; gold bands; black lettering	Quart/133	35.00	45.00	28.00
12.	Cognac	Black; gold bands; black lettering	Quart/133	35.00	45.00	28.00
13.	Gin	White; gold/blue bands; black lettering	Quart/133	35.00	45.00	28.00
14.	Port	White; gold/maroon bands; black lettering	Quart/133	5.00	45.00	28.00
15.	Scotch	White; gold/red bands; black lettering	Quart/133	35.00	45.00	28.00
16.	Sherry	White; gold/red/green bands; black lettering	Quart/133	35.00	45.00	28.00

Derivative

WINE BARREL LAMP

Early in 1958 Mr. Jasper Grinling, the Design Director of W. & A. Gilbey Limited, was asked to suggest a novelty design decanter in time for the 1958 Christmas season. A collector of Victorian wine barrels, Mr. Grinling suggested the wine barrel. When first issued in 1958, the barrels were intended only as a Christmas giftware line but proved to be so popular that the production run was extended for another three years until 1961. A lamp holder conversion kit and five different Gilbey lamp shades were launched in March 1959 at the Ideal Home Exhibition held every year in London, England.

Backstamp: Gold printed "Royal Victoria Pottery, Wade England"

No.	Description	Colourways	Shape/Size	U.S.$	Can.$	U.K.£
1.	Barrel Lamp	Black; gold bands, lettering "Cognac V.S.O.P white lamp fittings"	Quart/133	38.00	58.00	32.00

GILLESPIE'S STOUT

ASHTRAY, 1994-1996

Photograph not available
at press time

Backstamp: "Wade P D M Made in England"

No.	Description	Colourways	Shape/Size	U.S.$	Can.$	U.K.£
1.	Ashtray	Dark blue; multi-coloured lettering "Gillespie's Malt Stout"	Oval/171	15.00	20.00	8.00

GLEN EAGLE SCOTCH WHISKY

WATER JUG

This squat round shaped water jug has an open spout. A transfer print of an eagle's head is on the front, along with the words "Glen Eagle Scotch Whisky."

Backstamp: Printed "Wade pdm England" (pdm joined 1969-1984)

No.	Description	Colourways	Shape/Size	U.S.$	Can.$	U.K.£
1.	Water Jug	Amber jug; black eagle's head print/lettering "Glen Eagle Scotch Whisky"	Round/130	35.00	45.00	20.00

GLEN ELGIN
WHITE HORSE CELLAR

WATER JUG

Backstamp: Red printed "Wade PDM England" (pdm joined 1969-1984)

No.	Description	Colourways	Shape/Size	U.S.$	Can.$	U.K.£
1.	Water Jug	Dark brown; gold lettering "Aged 12 years Glen Elgin Pure Highland Malt Scotch Whisky"	Round/145	35.00	40.00	15.00

GLENGOYNE SCOTCH WHISKY

DRINK POURER

Backstamp: Unknown

No.	Description	Colourways	Shape/Size	U.S.$	Can.$	U.K.£
1.	Drink Pourer	Black; metal spout, neck; White/gold lettering "Glengoyne Single Highland Malt Scotch Whisky"	C57/29 x 60 Rectangular	30.00	35.00	12.00

GLEN GRANT HIGHLAND MALT SCOTCH WHISKY

DRINK POURER

Backstamp: Unknown

No.	Description	Colourways	Shape/Size	U.S.$	Can.$	U.K.£
1.	Drink Pourer	Cream; plastic spout, neck; black lettering "Aged 12 Years Glen Grant Highland Malt Scotch Whisky"	C53A/40 x 44 Oval	25.00	30.00	12.00

GLENLIVET WHISKY

DRINK POURERS, c.1990

This pourer was modelled in the shape of a golf ball.

Drink Pourer (No.2)

No.	Description	Colourways	Shape/Size	U.S.$	Can.$	U.K.£
1.	Drink Pourer	White; black lettering "The Glenlivet"	Round/40	40.00	45.00	20.00
2.	Drink Pourer	Cream; plastic spout, neck; black lettering "The Glenlivet George & J. G. Smith"	C52A/40 x 48 Octagonal	25.00	30.00	12.00

GLENMORANGIE HIGHLAND MALT

DRINK POURER

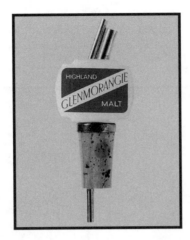

Backstamp: Impressed "C52A" under porcelain button, not seen unless pourer is taken apart

No.	Description	Colourways	Shape/Size	U.S.$	Can.$	U.K.£
1.	Drink Pourer	White/red; metal spout, neck; lettering "Highland Glenmorangie Malt"	C52A/40 x 48 Octagonal	30.00	35.00	12.00

GLEN ORD SCOTCH WHISKY

DRINK POURER

Backstamp: None

No.	Description	Colourways	Shape/Size	U.S.$	Can.$	U.K.£
1.	Drink Pourer	Black; metal spout, neck; white lettering "Glen Ord Single Malt Aged 12 Years"	C53/41 x 44 Round	30.00	35.00	120.00

GLENTURRET SCOTCH WHISKY
GLENTURRET DISTILLERIES

DECANTERS, 1991-1998

The circular 75-centilitre "Globe Decanter" was filled with 25-year-old Glenturret Whisky. It has an embossed map of the world around it. The "Copper Lustre Flagon," also 75 centilitres, contained Glenturrets 21-year-old blend of whisky. The Glenturret "Globe Decanter"and the "Copper Lustre Flagon," filled with 70 cl of Glenturret Whisky, could be purchased direct from Glenturret by mail order for £95.00 each up to December 1998.

"Globe Decanter"   "Copper Lustre Flagon"

Backstamp: A. "Genuine Wade Porcelain"
B. Transfer printed "Wade pdm England" in a circle (pdm separate 1984-1990)

No.	Item	Colourways	Size	U.S.$	Can.$	U.K.£
1.	Decanter	Blue/green; gold/white lettering; "75cl The Glenturret Rare Single Highland Malt Scotch Whisky"	195	85.00	105.00	45.00
2.	Flagon	Copper; gold/white lettering "The Glenturret"	195	80.00	100.00	40.00

DRINK POURER

Backstamp: Unmarked

No.	Item	Colourways	Size	U.S.$	Can.$	U.K.£
1.	Drink Pourer	Black; plastic spout, neck; white/gold lettering "Glenturret Established 1775 Single Highland Malt Scotch Whisky"	C53A/40 x 44 Oval	25.00	30.00	10.00

GORDON HIGHLANDER LTD.

DECANTER, 1987

Backstamp: "The Fox hunting Decanter is made by The Royal Victoria Pottery, Staffordshire, England Designed by Gordon Highlander Ltd.Collectors series"

No.	Description	Colourways	Shape/Size	U.S.$	Can.$	U.K.£
1.	Decanter	White; multi-coloured prints; black lettering	Hexagonal/255	80.00	100.00	40.00

GORDON'S GIN
UNITED DISTILLERS UK PLC

ASHTRAY AND WATER JUGS, 1968-1990

Water jugs were produced between 1968 and 1990. Both have ice-check spouts.

Backstamp: A. "Reginald Corfield Limited Redhill Surrey," "Wade Regicor England"
B. "Wade p d m England"

No.	Description	Colourways	Shape/Size	U.S.$	Can.$	U.K.£
1.	Ashtray	Yellow; red/black lettering; "Gordon's Special Dry Gin"	Square/155	15.00	20.00	8.00
2.	Water Jug	Yellow; red lettering "Gordon's Gin"	Rectangular/127	25.00	30.00	12.00
3.	Water Jug	Yellow; red print, lettering; "Gordon's Special London Dry Gin"	Square/130	35.00	45.00	20.00

DRINK POURERS

The octagonal pourers are shape number 5455/1. The square pourers, shape C52A, have a notched base and shoulders. The circular pourer is shape C53 and has a straight base.

Drink Pourer (No.2)

Drink Pourer (No.3)

Drink Pourer (No.4)

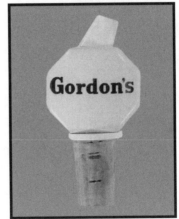
Drink Pourer (No.5)

Backstamp: **A.** "Wade Regicor Made in UK" on neck of pourer
B. Impressed "C52A" under porcelain button, not seen unless pourer is taken apart
C. Impressed "5455/1" on underside of button

No.	Description	Colourways	Shape/Size	U.S.$	Can.$	U.K.£
1.	Drink Pourer	White; plastic tube; green lettering; "Gordon's"	Circular/41	30.00	35.00	15.00
2.	Drink Pourer	White/green; metal spout, tube; white lettering "Gordon's"	C53/41 x 44 Circular	25.00	30.00	12.00
3.	Drink Pourer	White/yellow; metal spout, tube; red lettering "Gordon's Gin"	C52A/40 x 48 Octagonal	25.00	30.00	12.00
4.	Drink Pourer	White/yellow; plastic spout, neck; red lettering "Gordon's Gin"	Octagonal/40 x 47	25.00	30.00	12.00
5.	Drink Pourer	White; plastic spout, neck; green lettering "Gordon's"	Octagonal/40 x 47	25.00	30.00	12.00
6.	Drink Pourer	Yellow; red boar's head; plastic spout, neck; red lettering "Gordon's Estd 1769 London Dry Gin"	Octagonal/40 x 47	30.00	35.00	15.00

DRINK POURERS

Drink Pourer (No.8)

No.	Description	Colourways	Shape/Size	U.S.$	Can.$	U.K.£
7.	Drink Pourer	White; metal tube; dark green lettering; "Gordon's"	Square/48	30.00	35.00	15.00
8.	Drink Pourer	White; metal tube; red lettering; "Gordon's Gin"	Square/48	30.00	35.00	15.00

GRAND MACNISH SCOTCH WHISKY
MACNISH SCOTCH WHISKY

ASHTRAYS AND WATER JUG, 1955-1990

The ashtrays were produced between 1955 and 1984. The water jug, produced between 1984 and 1990, has an ice-check spout.

Ashtray "Grand Macnish Soctch Whisky"

Backstamp: A. "Wade Regicor, London England," laurel leaves, large size
B. "Wade Regicor, London England," laurel leaves, small size
C. "Wade p d m England"
D. "Wade pdm England, 86 Proof Blended Scotch Whisky Maidstone Importers Los Angeles California"

No.	Description	Colourways	Shape/Size	U.S.$	Can.$	U.K.£
1.	Ashtray	Primrose yellow; black/red lettering "Macnish"	Round/140	15.00	20.00	8.00
2.	Ashtray	White; black lettering "Macnish is Grand Scotch Whisky"	Round/140	15.00	20.00	8.00
3.	Ashtray	Yellow; black/red lettering "Grand Macnish"	Round/165	10.00	15.00	5.00
4.	Water Jug	Yellow; red/black lettering "Grand Macnish Scotch Whisky"	Round/140	35.00	45.00	20.00

GRANT'S SCOTCH WHISKY
WILLIAM GRANT & SONS LTD., THE GLENFIDDICH DISTILLERY

GRANT'S ASHTRAYS, 1955-1962

Ashtray, square with clipped corners

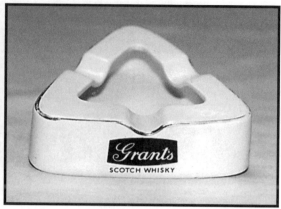

Ashtray, triangular

Backstamp: "Wade Regicor, London England," laurel leaves, large size

No.	Description	Colourways	Shape/Size	U.S.$	Can.$	U.K.£
1.	Ashtray	Black; gold lettering "Grant's Scotch Whisky"	Square/140 clipped corners	20.00	20.00	8.00
2.	Ashtray	White; red/white lettering "Grant's Scotch Whisky"	Triangular/115	15.00	20.00	8.00
3.	Ashtray	White; red/white lettering "Grant's Scotch Whisky"	Triangular/140	15.00	20.00	8.00

GLENFIDDISH DRINK POURER

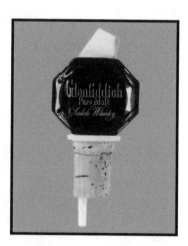

Backstamp: Impressed "5455/1" on underside of button

No.	Description	Colourways	Shape/Size	U.S.$	Can.$	U.K.£
1.	Drink Pourer	Black; plastic spout, neck; white lettering "Glenfiddich Pure Malt Scotch Whisky"	Octagonal/40 x 47	25.00	30.00	10.00

GLENFIDDICH DECANTERS, 1955-1962, 1991-1992

Two types of decanter have been reported: an octagonal with a thistle-shaped stopper and a round/bulbous one. Both have ornate gold decoration.

Bulbous Decanters

The 700-millilitre bulbous decanters were issued between 1991 and 1992. They resemble 18th century brandy bottles, with gold-coloured caps and gold leaf decoration. They contained 18-year-old Glenfiddich Whisky.

Decanter (No.3)   Decanter (No.4)

Backstamp: A. Printed "Wade Regicor London England," laurel leaf frame (large size 18 x 20mm 1953-1962)
B. Gold printed "Specially Commissioned by William Grant & Sons Ltd The Glenfiddich Distillery Scotland"

No.	Description	Colourways	Shape/Size	U.S.$	Can.$	U.K.£
1.	Decanter	Black; gold decoration, lettering "Single Glenfiddich Malt Aged 18 Years Scotch Whisky"	Bulbous/225	40.00	52.00	25.00
2.	Decanter	Dark green; gold decoration, lettering "Single Glenfiddich Malt Aged 18 Years Scotch Whisky"	Bulbous/225	40.00	52.00	25.00
3.	Decanter	Royal blue; gold decoration, lettering "Single Glenfiddich Malt Aged 18 Years Scotch Whisky"	Bulbous/225	40.00	52.00	25.00
4.	Decanter	Royal blue; gold decoration and lettering "Single Glenfiddich Malt Aged 18 Years Scotch Whisky"	Bulbous/100	25.00	35.00	12.00

Octagonal Decanters

No.	Description	Colourways	Shape/Size	U.S.$	Can.$	U.K.£
1.	Decanter	Black; gold decoration; gold/white lettering "Single Malt Glenfiddich Heritage Reserve Scotch Whisky"	Octagonal/215	40.00	52.00	25.00
2.	Decanter	Royal blue; gold decoration; gold/white lettering "Single Malt Glenfiddich Heritage Reserve Scotch Whisky"	Octagonal/215	40.00	52.00	25.00
3.	Decanter	Dark green; gold decoration; gold/white lettering "Single Malt Glenfiddich Heritage Reserve Scotch Whisky"	Octagonal/215	40.00	52.00	25.00

WATER JUGS, 1955-1992

The water jug which has an ice-check spout was produced between 1955 and 1962.

Water Jug (No.4)

Backstamp: **A.** "Wade Regicor, London England," laurel leaves, large size
B. Printed "Wade pdm England" (pdm joined 1969-1984)
C. Gold printed "Specially Commissioned by William Grant & Sons Ltd The Glenfiddich Distillery Scotland"

No.	Description	Colourways	Shape/Size	U.S.$	Can.$	U.K.£
1.	Water Jug	White; red/white lettering "Grant's Scotch Whisky"	Triangular/165	30.00	45.00	20.00
2.	Water Jug	Royal blue; gold lettering "Grant's Scotch Whisky"	Round/153	35.00	40.00	20.00
3.	Water Jug	Maroon; gold print, lettering "Grant's Royal Scotch Whisky"	Round/153	35.00	40.00	20.00
4.	Water Jug	Royal blue; gold decoration, lettering "Single Malt Glenfiddich Aged 18 Years Scotch Whisky"	Round/153	35.00	40.00	18.00

GREENALL WHITLEY

ASHTRAYS AND DRINK POURER, 1969-1996

The print on the No. 1 ashtray is of a woman.

Backstamp: A. "Wade pdm England"
B. "Wade P D M Made in England"
C. Impressed "5455/1" on underside of pourer button

No.	Description	Colourways	Shape/Size	U.S.$	Can.$	U.K.£
1.	Ashtray	Dark green; yellow/grey/red print; yellow lettering "Greenall Whitley"	Round/205	10.00	15.00	5.00
2.	Ashtray	Dark green; yellow lettering "Greenall's Original"	Square/101	10.00	15.00	5.00
3.	Drink Pourer	Red/white; plastic tube, spout; "Greenall's 1761 London Dry Gin"	Octagonal/40 x 47	25.00	30.00	10.00

GREENE KING

ASHTRAYS AND WATER JUG, 1968-1984

The jug has an open spout and a print on it of a king's head.

Ashtray (No,2)

Ashtray (No.4)

Water Jug (No.5)

Backstamp: A. "Reginald Corfield Limited Redhill Surrey," "Wade Regicor England"
B. "Wade pdm England"

No.	Description	Colourways	Shape/Size	U.S.$	Can.$	U.K.£
1.	Ashtray	Olive green; yellow lettering "Greene King"	Round/127	15.00	20.00	8.00
2.	Ashtray	Dark green; yellow lettering "Greene King"	Round/195	15.00	20.00	8.00
3.	Ashtray	White; red/black lettering "Greene King Abbot Ale"	Square/146	15.00	20.00	8.00
4.	Ashtray	Dark green; yellow lettering	Square/140	12.00	15.00	8.00
5.	Water Jug	Dark green; gold print, lettering "Greene King"	Round/101	30.00	35.00	18.00

GUARDS HEAVY

ASHTRAY

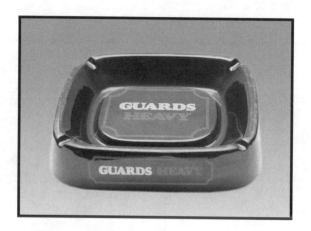

Backstamp: Printed circular "Wade pdm" (pdm joined 1969-1984)

No.	Description	Colourways	Shape/Size	U.S.$	Can.$	U.K.£
1.	Ashtray	Black; red/white lettering "Guards Heavy"	Square/215	8.00	10.00	6.00

GUINNESS

ASHTRAY, c.1990-1996

Photograph not available
at press time

Backstamp: "Wade P D M Made in England"

No.	Description	Colourways	Size	U.S.$	Can.$	U.K.£
1.	Ashtray	Black; gold lettering "Guinness"	Round/216	20.00	28.00	8.00

CIGARETTE BOXES, c.1958-c.1960

Style No. 1 was produced by Wade Ireland in the late 1950s. On the sides and lid it is decorated with an embossed design of whales in a frame of knurls. In the centre of the lid is a transfer print of the Mayflower, from the 1956-1957 Snippets series. On the inside of the box is an embossed poem extolling the virtues of drinking Guinness.

The Guinness Cigarette Box was issued in the 1960s. It has a print of a horse-drawn bus on the lid with the words "Guinness one of the Best Cordials not in the Pharmacopoeiathe lancet 1837."

Wade Ireland Cigarette Box

Backstamp: **A.** "Irish Porcelain, Made in Ireland by Wade Co. Armagh"
B. "Wade England"

No.	Description	Colourways	Size	U.S.$	Can.$	U.K.£
1..	Guinness	Black; white lid; multi-coloured print; black lettering	55 x 140	70.00	90.00	35.00
2.	Wade Ireland	Grey/blue; multi-coloured print	45 x 125	70.00	90.00	35.00

PEANUT BOWLS, c.1962

Kangaroo Peanut Dish

Pelican Peanut Dish

Sea Lion Peanut Dish

Toucann Peanut Dish

Backstamp: "Wade Regicor, London England," laurel leaves, small size

No.	Description	Colourways	Shape/Size	U.S.$	Can.$	U.K.£
1.	Kangaroo	Pale green; multi-coloured kangaroo	Round/35	50.00	65.00	30.00
2.	Pelican	Pale blue; multi-coloured pelican	Round/35	50.00	65.00	30.00
3.	Sea Lion	Yellow; multi-coloured sea lion	Round/35	50.00	65.00	30.00
4.	Toucan	Light grey; multi-coloured toucan	Round/35	50.00	65.00	30.00

G. W. ARCHER'S ORIGINAL PEACH SCHNAPPS

DRINK POURERS

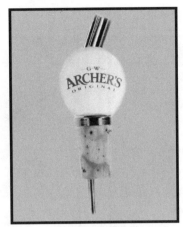

Drink Pourer (No.1)

Backstamp: None

No.	Description	Colourways	Shape/Size	U.S.$	Can.$	U.K.£
1.	Drink Pourer	White; metal spout, tube; black/red lettering "G. W. Archer's Original"	Round C53/41 x 44	25.00	30.00	12.00
2.	Drink Pourer	White; metal spout, tube; red lettering "Archer's"	Round C53/41 x 44	25.00	30.00	12.00

HAIG SCOTCH WHISKY

DRINK POURERS AND WATER JUG, 1984-1990

These drink pourers, shape C53, have a straight base. The water jug, which was produced between 1984 and 1990, has an open spout.

Drink Pourer (No.2)

Drink Pourer (No.3)

Backstamp: "Wade p d m England"

No.	Description	Colourways	Shape/Size	U.S.$	Can.$	U.K.£
1.	Drink Pourer	White/red button; black lettering "Haig"	Circular/41	30.00	35.00	15.00
2.	Drink Pourer	White/red; metal spout, neck; black lettering "Haig"	C53/41 x 44 Round	25.00	30.00	12.00
3.	Drink Pourer	White/red; plastic spout, neck; black lettering "Haig"	C53A/40 x 44 Oval	25.00	30.00	12.00
4.	Water Jug	White; gold lettering "Haig The Oldest Name in Scotch Whisky"	Rectangular/169	30.00	35.00	18.00

HARP LAGER

ASHTRAYS, 1955-1990

Ashtray (No.5)

Ashtray (No.6)

Backstamp: **A.** "Wade Regicor, London England," laurel leaves, large size
B. "Wade Regicor, London England," laurel leaves, small size
C. "Reginald Corfield Limited Redhill Surrey," "Wade Regicor England"
D. "Wade p d m England"

No.	Description	Colourways	Shape/Size	U.S.$	Can.$	U.K.£
1.	Ashtray	White/royal blue; white/blue/yellow lettering "Harp"	Round/177	15.00	20.00	8.00
2.	Ashtray	White/blue; white/blue/yellow lettering "Keg Harp Lager"	Round/177	15.00	20.00	8.00
3.	Ashtray	Blue/white; white print; black/yellow lettering "Keg Harp Lager"	Hexagonal/146	15.00	20.00	8.00
4.	Ashtray	Cream; white/black lettering "Harp Golden Lager"	Triangular/177	25.00	30.00	12.00
5.	Ashtray	Dark blue; white and white print; white lettering "Harp Lager"	Triangular/185	25.00	30.00	12.00
6.	Ashtray	White/royal blue; white lettering "Harp Lager"	Round/182	15.00	20.00	8.00

HEDGES AND BUTLER SCOTCH WHISKY

DRINK POURER

Backstamp: Red printed "Wade England"

No.	Description	Colourways	Shape/Size	U.S.$	Can.$	U.K.£
1.	Drink Pourer	White; metal spout, tube, dust cover; black lion print/lettering "1667 Hedges & Butler Royal Scotch Whisky"	Circular/BIG1/62	35.00	40.00	18.00

WATER JUG

Backstamp: Gold Printed "Fine Staffordshire Pottery Duncan Fox & Co. Inc. New York Regicor Wade 86 Proof Blended Scotch Whisky Imported by the Westminster Corporation New York N.Y."

No.	Description	Colourways	Shape/Size	U.S.$	Can.$	U.K.£
1.	Water Jug	Black; gold lettering "Hedges & Butler Royal Scotch"	Round/160	35.00	40.00	18.00

HEINEKEN LAGER

ASHTRAY, 1969-1984

The print on this ashtray depicts a tower and mountains.

Photograph not available
at press time

Backstamp: "Wade pdm England"

No.	Description	Colourways	Shape/Size	U.S.$	Can.$	U.K.£
1.	Ashtray	Green; multi-coloured print; white lettering "Heineken Lager"	Oval/229	15.00	20.00	8.00

HENNESSY FINE COGNAC

DRINK POURER

Backstamp: Impressed "5455/1" on underside of button

No.	Description	Colourways	Shape/Size	U.S.$	Can.$	U.K.£
1.	Drink Pourer	Cream; plastic spout, neck; gold vine leaves and lettering "Hennessy Fine Cognac"	Octagonal/40 x 47	20.00	25.00	10.00

HENRY STRATTON AND CO. LTD.

SPIRIT CONTAINERS, 1961

The George Wade Pottery was commissioned to produce a set of five liqueur and spirit containers for a small British distillery, Henry Stratton and Co. Ltd. of Bolton. Before Wade finished the production run and Henry Stratton and Co. Ltd. had taken delivery of all models, the distillery was destroyed by fire. The remaining containers were sold for 1/- each to Boots The Chemist, which retailed them in its giftware departments. Some of the containers are now known to have been sold off to other liqueur distributers: the "Chick" and the medium- sized "Penguin" have been found with labels from Rawlings & Sons and Wyld & Co. The original Henry Stratton containers (of which there are a limited number) are found with white paper labels bearing the name of the liqueur inside and "Henry Stratton & Co. Ltd., Bolton." The original stoppers were plastic topped corks, although some have been found with plain corks. To date the "Cockatoo" container has not been reported with a liqueur label.

Penguins

Chick

Cockatoo

Backstamp: A. Chick — Paper label "Guernsey Cream Advocaat (30% Proof) Henry Stratton & Co Ltd., Bolton"
B. Penguin, small — Paper label "Contains Finest Creme De Menthe Produce of France (44% proof) Henry Stratton & Co. Ltd., Bolton"
C. Penguin, medium — Paper label "Contains Choice Old Port Produce of Portugal Henry Stratton & Co. Ltd., Bolton"
D. Penguin, large — Paper label "Finest Cherry Brandy 42% proof Henry Stratton & Co. Ltd., Bolton"
E. Chick — Paper label "Guernsey Cream, Advocaat, Channel Islands Fine Distillers Ltd, Guernsey. Sole Concessionaire Rawlings & Son (London) Ltd."
F. Penguin, medium — Paper label "Wylds Bristol Milk-Choice Golden Sherry Wyld & Co. Ltd., Bristol 1"

No.	Name	Colourways	Size	U.S.$	Can.$	U.K.£
1.	Chick	Yellow; black eyes, brown beak, toes, green/yellow base	87	70.00	80.00	30.00
2.	Cockatoo	White; yellow crest; green mottled base	130	150.00	195.00	100.00
3.	Penguin, small	Blue-grey/white; blue/green base	95	38.00	50.00	22.00
4.	Penguin, medium	Blue-grey/white; blue/green base	115	45.00	70.00	25.00
5.	Penguin, large	Blue-grey/white; blue/green base	118	50.00	75.00	35.00

HIGH AND DRY GIN

ASHTRAY AND DRINK POURER, 1955-1962

Backstamp: **A.** "Wade Regicor, London England," laurel leaves, large size
B. Impressed "5455/1" on underside of button

No.	Description	Colourways	Shape/Size	U.S.$	Can.$	U.K.£
1.	Ashtray	White; black lettering "High & Dry Gin"	Square/140	15.00	20.00	8.00
2.	Drink Pourer	White; plastic spout, neck; black lettering "High & Dry Gin"	Octagonal/40 x 47	25.00	30.00	12.00

HIGHLAND QUEEN SCOTCH WHISKY

ASHTRAY, DRINK POURER AND WATER JUG, 1955-1962

Backstamp: A. "Wade Regicor, London England," laurel leaves, large size
B. Impressed "5455/1" on underside of button
C. Printed circular "Wade pdm" (pdm joined 1969-1984)

No.	Description	Colourways	Shape/Size	U.S.$	Can.$	U.K.£
1.	Ashtray	Black; red lettering "Highland Queen"	Round/140	15.00	20.00	8.00
2.	Drink Pourer	White; plastic spout, neck; green lettering "Highland Queen Scotch Whisky"	Octagonal/40 x 47	25.00	30.00	12.00
3.	Water Jug, open spout	Maroon; gold print, lettering "Highland Queen Fine Old Scotch Whisky"	Round/120	35.00	40.00	18.00

HINE COGNAC

DRINK POURER

Backstamp: Impressed "5455/1" on underside of button

No.	Description	Colourways	Shape/Size	U.S.$	Can.$	U.K.£
1.	Drink Pourer	White; plastic spout, neck; brown hine (stag) print; brown lettering "Hine Cognac"	Octagonal/40 x 47	25.00	30.00	12.00

HOLSTEIN

PINT SIZE TRADITIONAL TANKARD

Photograph not available
at press time

Backstamp: Printed "Wade England"

No.	Description	Colourways	Shape/Size	U.S.$	Can.$	U.K.£
1.	Tankard	Grey; multi-coloured knight on horse print; red/black lettering "Holstein Export"	114	15.00	18.00	9.00

HOOK NORTON ALES

ASHTRAY, 1955-1962

Backstamp: "Wade Regicor, London England," laurel leaves, large size

No.	Description	Colourways	Shape/Size	U.S.$	Can.$	U.K.£
1.	Ashtray	Pale green; yellow print, green lettering "Hook Norton Ales"	Round/133	15.00	20.00	8.00

HOUSE OF LORDS SCOTCH WHISKY
WILLIAM WHITELEY & CO. DISTILLERS

ASHTRAY

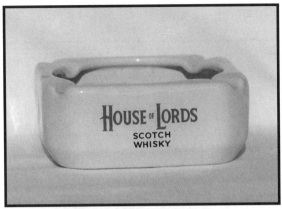

Ashtray (No. 1)

Backstamp: Transfer print "Wade pdm England" (pdm joined 1969-1984)

No.	Description	Colourways	Shape/Size	U.S.$	Can.$	U.K.£
1.	Ashtray	Creamy yellow; red/black lettering "House of Lords Scotch Whisky"	Rectangular/153	10.00	15.00	8.00

WATER JUGS

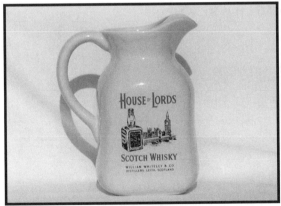

Water Jug (No. 2)

Water Jug (No. 3)

Backstamp: Transfer print "Wade pdm England" (pdm joined 1969-1984)

No.	Description	Colourways	Shape/Size	U.S.$	Can.$	U.K.£
1.	Water Jug, ice-check spout	Creamy yellow; black print; red/black lettering "House of Lords Scotch Whisky"	Rectangular/165	35.00	40.00	18.00
2.	Water Jug, ice-check spout	Creamy yellow; red/black lettering "House of Lords 8 Years Old Scotch Whisky William Whiteley & Co Distillers Pitlochry Scotland"	Rectangular/165	35.00	40.00	18.00

HOUSE OF PEERS SCOTCH WHISKY
DOUGLAS LAING & CO. LTD. GLASGOW

WATER JUG

This square-shaped jug has a small open spout.

Backstamp: Printed "Wade pdm England" (pdm joined 1969-1984)

No.	Description	Colourways	Shape/Size	U.S.$	Can.$	U.K.£
1.	Water Jug	Black; white print, lettering "House of Peers Finest Scotch Whisky Douglas Laing & Co, Ltd, Glasgow"	114	35.00	40.00	18.00

HUDSONS BAY SCOTCH WHISKY

ASHTRAY, 1968-1969

Photograph not available
at press time

Backstamp: "Reginald Corfield, London England," "Wade Regicor England"

No.	Description	Colourways	Shape/Size	U.S.$	Can.$	U.K.£
1.	Ashtray	White; black lettering "Hudsons Bay Scotch Whisky"	Round/159	15.00	20.00	8.00

HUNTS MIXERS & FRUIT JUICES

DRINK POURERS

Drink Pourer (No.2)

Backstamp: Impressed "5455/1" on underside of porcelain button

No.	Description	Colourways	Shape/Size	U.S.$	Can.$	U.K.£
1.	Drink Pourer	White/dark green; plastic spout, neck; white lettering (front) "Hunts Mixers" (back) "Hunts Fruit Juices"	Octagonal/40 x 47	25.00	30.00	10.00
2.	Drink Pourer	White/black; plastic spout, neck; white lettering "Hunts Mixers"	Octagonal/40 x 47	25.00	30.00	10.00

IMPERIAL VODKA

WATER JUG, 1962-1968

This water jug, which has an open spout, is decorated with a print of a large double-headed eagle.

Photograph not available
at press time

Backstamp: "Wade Regicor, London England," laurel leaves, small size

No.	Description	Colourways	Shape/Size	U.S.$	Can.$	U.K.£
1.	Water Jug, open spout	Royal blue; black print; yellow/white/blue lettering "Imperial Vodka Taplows Ltd London"	Round/165	38.00	50.00	15.00

IND COOPE'S

ASHTRAYS

This ashtray has an Ind Coope's Burton Ale label in the centre and the words "Burton Ale Traditional Strong Ale" around the sides.

Ashtray (No.2)

Backstamp: A. Transfer print "Wade pdm England" (pdm 1969-1984)
B. Transfer printed "Wade pdm England" (pdm separate 1984-1990)

No.	Description	Colourways	Shape/Size	U.S.$	Can.$	U.K.£
1.	Ashtray	White; gold rim; blue centre; white lettering "Ind Coope's Hotels"	Round/115	8.00	10.00	4.00
2.	Ashtray	White/grey speckled; multi-coloured label; white/gold /red lettering "Ind Coope's Burton Ale Brewed at Burton Burton Ale Traditional Strong Ale"	Oval/190 long	20.00	25.00	12.00

INTERNATIONAL ASSOCIATION OF JIM BEAM BOTTLES
& SPECIALTIES CLUB

For more than thirty years the Regal China Company produced decorative bottles and decanters for the International Association of Jim Beam Bottles & Specialties Club—IAJBBSC—for member's exclusive use. In 1992 Regal China closed down, and it was in 1993 that Wade made their first decanter for the IAJBBSC. The items are listed under various categories: club convention items; district meetings; and German Beamers Club. Note that there were no items produced for the German Beamers Club in 1997, 1998 or 1999.

Surplus IAJBBSC/John Paul Jones decanters with blue stoppers and white stoppers and surplus blue and white John Paul Jones jugs were offered for sale to members of the International Wade Collectors Club in 1996 at a price of $75 US for the decanters and $62.00 U.S for the jugs. The green jugs were not offered to International Wade Club collectors as they were all sold as fund raisers to IAJBBSC members only. (For "John Paul Jones" decanters without the IAJBBSC backstamp and with a "Splice the Main Brace" Pusser's Rum label on the top of the stopper, see Pusser's Rum, page 225).

23RD ANNUAL CONVENTION, CHARLOTTE, N.C., 1993

John Paul Jones Ships Decanters

This one-litre decanter was produced for the 1993 convention of the International Association of Jim Beam Bottle and Specialties Club in Charlotte, North Carolina. It is from the same mould as the Admiral Lord Nelson decanter (page 225), but the decorations were changed to show scenes honouring John Paul Jones and the United States Navy and Marine Corps. Nine hundred decanters were produced: 450 with cobalt blue stoppers and 450 with white stoppers. The IAJBBSC logo is printed on a label in the recess on the stoppers of the decanter and the jugs.

Backstamp: A. "1993 Convention of the International Association of Jim Beam Bottle & Specialties Club, Charlotte, North Carolina, Wade"
B. Printed "23rd Annual Convention I.A.J.B.B.S.C. Charlotte North Carolina July 18-23 1993 Wade Porcelain England 'Pusser's LTD British Virgin Islands, West Indies Handcaste & Hand Decorated Made In England' 'The John Paul Jones' U.S. Navy and Marine Corps Ships Decanter Genuine Wade Porcelain"

No.	Description	Colourways	Size	U.S.$	Can.$	U.K.£
1.	Decanter	Blue decanter, stopper; multi-coloured prints	220	125.00	165.00	75.00
2.	Decanter	Blue decanter; white stopper; multi-coloured prints	220	125.00	165.00	75.00

President's Gift to Chair Persons

Seventy-five extra-large cups and saucers were produced for the IAJBBSC as the president's expression of appreciation to committee chair persons at the Charlotte, N.C., Convention. The back is inscribed "Thank you for your support at the 1993 Convention," and both the cup and the saucer have the facsimile signature of the IAJBBSC President Ron Danner. The logo depicted on the race car on the front of the cup is Foxy [©]. The cup and saucer is from a mould originally produced for Boots The Chemist (see *The Charlton Standard Catalogue of Wade Tablewares, Volume 3, 2nd Edition*). (Note: None of the presidents gifts were for sale.)

Cup & Saucer (front)

Cup & Saucer (back)

Backstamp: Black printed "Wade England" within two lines

No.	Description	Colourways	Size	U.S.$	Can.$	U.K.£
1.	Foxy [©] Cup/Saucer	White; blue Foxy in race car; logo "Thank You For Your Support At The 1993 Convention"	Extra Large 88/195	120.00	160.00	80.00

24*TH* ANNUAL CONVENTION, 1994

President's Gift to Chair Persons

One hundred cookie cars were produced for the IAJBBSC as the president's gift to committee chair persons. The jar is from the same mould as the 1993 Kings Kitchen Ware storage jar (see The *Charlton Standard Catalogue of Wade Tablewares, Volume 3, 2nd Edition*) and has an embossed Leaf design. On the front is a blue Foxy in the Beam Bi-Plane cartoon logo © R.Ellis and is inscribed "Thank you." The back is inscribed "Thank you For Your Support At The 1994 Convention," and both the jar and the lid have the facsimile signature of Ron Danner.

Cookie Jar (front)

Cookie Jar (back)

Backstamp: Printed "Wade England" with two lines

No.	Description	Colourways	Size	U.S.$	Can.$	U.K.£
1.	Cookie Jar	White; blue Foxy logo	205	75.00	90.00	45.00

GERMAN BEAMERS CLUB, 1994

This was the first jug-shaped whicky decanter issued by the German Beamer club. Only eighty-eight jugs were made.

Backstamp: Gold printed "Genuine Wade Porcelain"

No.	Description	Colourways	Size	U.S.$	Can.$	U.K.£
1.	Jug Decanter	Dark blue; gold 1957 Cadillac car print and lettering "German Beamer 8th Jan 1994 First German Club"	Square/200	55.00	65.00	30.00

25THANNIVERSARY CONVENTION, LOUISVILLE, KENTUCKY, 1995

Anniversary Barrels

This ceramic barrel was produced to celebrate the 200th anniversary of the Jim Beam Company, as well as the 25th Anniversary of the International Association of Jim Beam Bottle & Specialties Club. The 1995 convention was held at Louisville, Kentucky, USA.

There were a total of 1,750 barrels produced: 700 in cobalt blue, 700 in black, and 350 in dark green,

200th Anniversary Barrel (front)　　　　　　　　　　　200th Anniversary Barrel (back)

Backstamp: "Produced under licensing agreement with Jim Beams Brands, Wade Porcelain"

No.	Description	Colourways	Size	U.S.$	Can.$	U.K.£
1.	Barrel	Black; gold bands; multi-coloured print	224	100.00	140.00	55.00
2.	Barrel	Cobalt blue; gold bands; multi-coloured print	224	100.00	140.00	55.00
3.	Barrel	Dark green; gold bands; multi-coloured print	224	125.00	170.00	60.00

Coasters

Four coasters (produced in two colours) celebrating the 25th anniversary of the IAJBBSC were available to Jim Beam Bottle Club members at the Louisville Convention meeting held in July 1995. The original price for the coasters was $ 30.00 (U.S) for a boxed set of four. A total of 1,525 sets were produced.

Backstamp: Printed "Wade P D M Made in England" within two red lines

No.	Description	Colourways	Size	U.S.$	Can.$	U.K.£
1.	Coasters	Black; silver lettering; (set of four)	97	40.00	50.00	25.00
2.	Coasters	Cobalt blue; silver lettering; (set of four)	97	20.00	25.00	12.00

President's Gift to Chair Persons

A 25th Anniversary Teapot was produced as the president's gift to committee chair persons. The inscription on the back reads "Thank you For Your Support At Our 25th Convention 1995." The president's facsimile signature appears on both the back and lid of the teapot. On the front is an IAJBBSC cartoon logo of Foxy © holding glasses of champagne and the No. 25. The teapot is in the 1986-1995 Albert shape (see *The Charlton Standard Catalogue of Wade Tablewares, Volume 3, 2nd Edition*.)

Teapot (front)

Teapot (back)

Backstamp: Printed "Wade England" with two lines and the I.A.J.B.B.S.C. logo

No.	Description	Colourways	Size	U.S.$	Can.$	U.K.£
1.	Teapot	White; blue Foxy © with champagne glass logo and lettering	159	55.0	65.00	30.00

CLUB AWARDS, 1995

Charity Christmas Tree Teapot

In 1995 the Club awarded the 1990-1991 Wade "Christmas Tree" teapot. The teapot was given to each club that exceeded its charity ticket sales quotas during 1996. A total of 182 teapots were produced.

Photograph not available
at press time

Backstamp: Printed "I.A.J.B.B.S.C. Logo Wade"

No.	Description	Colourways	Size	U.S.$	Can.$	U.K.£
1.	Christmas Tree Teapot	White; gold star; multi-coloured print	146		Unknown	

Membership Christmas Tree Teapot

In 1995 a "Christmas Tree" teapot was given to each club that had maintained or exceeded it's previous year's membership level. Three hundred and eighty two teapots were produced.

Photograph not available
at press time

Backstamp: Printed "Membership Award 1995 I.A.J.B.B.S.C. logo" with "Wade" between two lines

No.	Description	Colourways	Size	U.S.$	Can.$	U.K.£
1.	Christmas Tree Teapot	Green; gold star; multi-coloured print	146		Unknown	

DISTRICT MEETINGS, 1995

Two thousand of these one-litre jugs were produced for the district meetings of the International Association of Jim Beam Bottle and Specialties Club: 900 blue, 750 white, and 350 green.

Jug (No.2)   Jug (No.3)

Backstamp: **A.** Printed "Genuine Wade Porcelain Limited Edition 900"
 B. Printed "Genuine Wade Porcelain Limited Edition 750"
 C. Printed "Genuine Wade Porcelain Limited Edition 350"

No.	Description	Colourways	Size	U.S.$	Can.$	U.K.£
1.	Jug	Blue/white jug, stopper; multi-coloured prints	200	55.00	65.00	30.00
2.	Jug	Green/white jug, stopper; multi-coloured prints	200	55.00	65.00	30.00
3.	Jug	White jug, stopper; multi-coloured prints	200	40.00	55.00	20.00

GERMAN BEAMERS CLUB, 1995

This jug-shaped whisky decanter was produced for the first anniversary of the German Beamers Club. The decal on the front reads "German Beamer First Club Germany" with a print of a 1957 Cadillac car; the decal on the back reads "Anniversary German Beamer Club 8th January 1995" with Cadillac car print. Only eighty jugs were produced. Original cost was $35.00 (U.S.).

Backstamp: Gold Printed "Genuine Wade Porcelain"

No.	Description	Colourways	Shape/Size	U.S.$	Can.$	U.K.£
1.	Jug Decanter	Dark green; gold print, lettering "German Beamer First German Club"	Square/200	55.00	65.00	30.00

26TH INTERNATIONAL I.A.J.B.B.S.C. CONVENTION AND FIRST U.S.A. WADE SHOW, SEATTLE, WASHINTON, 1996

Van Money Box

The "Van money box" was produced in a limited edition of 315 cream glaze and 305 in blue glaze. There were also 200 white vans produced which were sold to clubs only. The original cost of the vans was $45.00 (U.S.). Unsold vans were given as prizes in raffles. The van is from the same mould as the 1995 "Rington's Tea" "Van money box." (see *The Charlton Standard Catalogue of Wade, General Issues: Volume 1, 3rd Ed.*)

Van Money Box (No.1)

Van Money Box (No.3)

Backstamp: Black printed "I.A.J.B.B.S.C. 26th Annual Convention July 6-12 1996 Seattle Washington 1 of 300" "Wade England" with two lines and the IAJBBSC logo

No.	Description	Colourways	Size	U.S.$	Can.$	U.K.£
1.	Van Money Box	Blue	133 x 205	95.00	125.00	65.00
2.	Van Money Box	Cream	133 x 205	95.00	125.00	65.00
3.	Van Money Box	White	133 x 205	139.00	150.00	75.00

Seattle Space Needle Decanters

Only four models of this decanter in the shape of the famous Seattle Space Needle were commissioned by the IAJBBSC as prizes in their raffle, but on the day of the draw two decanters were dropped and broken. "Seattle" is impressed on the bottom rim. (Note: The actual Space Needle is supported by three legs, but the Wade decanter depicts it with four.)

Backstamp: Printed "Genuine Wade"

No.	Description	Colourways	Size	U.S.$	Can.$	U.K.£
1.	Space Needle	Green	229 x 127		Extremely Rare	
2.	Space Needle	Yellow	229 x 127		Extremely Rare	

Tea Tidy

The Tea Tidy is a flat teapot-shaped dish that serves to hold used teabags. It has a transfer print of the IAJBBSC/Wade mascot "Wade" in the centre with the words "Hi... I'm Wade."

Backstamp: Printed "Produced Exclusively for I.A.J.B.B.S.C. July 1996" with I.A.J.B.B.S.C./Wade logo and "Wade England" with two lines

No.	Description	Colourways	Size	U.S.$	Can.$	U.K.£
1.	Tea Tidy	Cream; dark blue print/lettering "Hi...I'm Wade"	95 x 120	20.00	25.00	12.00
2.	Tea Tidy	Blue; dark blue print/lettering "Hi.. I'm Wade"	95 x 120	20.00	25.00	12.00

President's Gift to Chair Persons

One hundred floral printed "Dainty Pear" shaped teapots, (the shape was originally used in the 1993 Regency Collection) were produced by Wade for the 1996 IAJBBSC Seattle Convention President's Gift to committee chair persons. The base is inscribed "Thank you for your support Seattle 1996, and has the signature *Jo-Anne.*

| Teapot (front) | Teapot (back) |

Backstamp: Printed "Thank You For Your Support, Seattle 1996" signed *Jo Anne.* "Wade" within two red lines

No.	Description	Colourways	Size	U.S.$	Can.$	U.K.£
1.	Teapot	White; multi-coloured flowers print	140	Unknown		

CLUB AWARDS, 1996

Charity: Water/Whisky Jug

This water/whisky jug was given to each club that exceeded its charity ticket sales quotas during 1996. Altogether, 175 jugs were produced.

Photograph not available
at press time

Backstamp: Unknown

No.	Description	Colourways	Shape/Size	U.S.$	Can.$	U.K.£
1.	Water Jug	Light blue; black/red rosette, logo and lettering	Round/Unknown		Unknown	

Membership Water/Whisky Jug

A water/whisky jug was given to each club that had maintained or exceeded it's previous year's membership level. One hundred and fifty jugs were produced.

Photograph not available
at press time

Backstamp: Unknown

No.	Description	Colourways		Shape/Size	U.S.$	Can.$	U.K.£
1.	Water Jug	Cream; black rosette, logo and lettering	Unknown	Unknown			

DISTRICT MEETINGS, 1996

The IAJBBSC mascot is Foxy, ^{© R.Ellis} a cartoon fox wearing a large black hat created by Dick Ellis. The teapots, which were produced in a limited edition of 750 blue, 612 cream, and 354 white, are decorated with transfer prints of cartoon characters of Ghost, Foxy, Mrs Foxy, Tiffany the poodle, and other animated Beam Bottle characters. The teapot is "Albert" shaped with the teapot lid finial redesigned as the mascots head. The teapots were only available to Jim Beam Club members attending district meetings. The original price for the teapot was $50.00 U.S.

Backstamp: Printed "Animated Characters Copyright R.Ellis 1995. All rights reserved.
Exclusively Produced For The I.A.J.B.B.S.C. Limited Edition 1 of 1700 By Wade"

No.	Description	Colourways	Size	U.S.$	Can.$	U.K.£
1.	Teapot	Blue; multi-coloured cartoon	165	55.00	65.00	35.00
2.	Teapot	Cream; multi- coloured cartoon	165	55.00	65.00	35.00
3.	Teapot	White; multi-coloured cartoon	165	55.00	65.00	35.00

GERMAN BEAMERS CLUB, 1996

Round Whiskey Jug Decanter

This jug-shaped whisky decanter was produced for the 2nd anniversary of the German Beamers Club. The decal on the front is Dreamer Beamers 2nd Anniversary German Beamer Club, with a print of a man in bed dreaming of a first National Decanter. *Dreamers Beamers* is the name of the U.S. sister club to the German club. The back decal shows a 1957 Cadillac car with the words "German Beamer First Club Germany." There is no date on this jug. Only eighty jugs were produced, with an original cost of $35.00

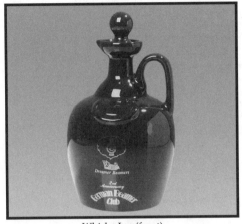

| Whisky Jug (front) | Whisky Jug (back) |

Backstamp: Gold printed "Genuine Wade Porcelain"

No.	Description	Colourways	Size	U.S.$	Can.$	U.K.£
1.	Whiskey Jug, Burgundy; gold 1957 Cadillac car print and gold lettering	Round/200	45.00	55.00	30.00

Square Whisky Jug Decanter

This square-shaped jug decanter has "German Beamer First Club Germany" with a 1957 Cadillac car decoration on one side, "Dreamer Beamers German Beamer Club" on the other, with a Christmas tree decal and the name *"WEIHNACHTEN 1996"* (Christmas 1996) on the front. Only eighty jugs were made.

| Whisky Jug, 1957 Cadillac car (side) | Whisky Jug, German Beamer Club (side) | "WEIHNACHTEN 1996" (front) |

Backstamp: Gold printed "Genuine Wade Porcelain"

No.	Description	Colourways	Size	U.S.$	Can.$	U.K.£
1.	Whiskey Jug, Burgundy; gold 1957 Cadillac car, print, lettering	Square/200	45.00	55.00	30.00

27TH INTERNATIONAL I.A.J.B.B.S.C. CONVENTION AND SECOND U.S.A. WADE SHOW, OKONOMOWOC, WISCONSIN, 1997

DECANTERS, 1997

Happy Little Guys Decanters

Because of increasing requests from the Jim Beam membership for decanters, a set of three decanters in the shape of smiling comic men were produced for the IAJBBSC. The decanters were also made available to Wade Collectors through the International Wade Club Magazine. On the front of the blue and yellow guy decanters is the profile of the Jim Beam Association's Mascot Foxy © R.Ellis and the words "Beam Bottle Collector." The third decanter is in the shape of the Jim Beam/Wade mascot Wade and has the name "Wade" on his front. All three bottles were designed by Dick Ellis. The bottles were sold at an original price of $50.00 (U.S.) each.

Backstamp: On the back of each decanter is a black printed circle consisting of the words "International Association of Jim Beam Bottle and Specialities Club" over an outline map of U.S.A. with the figure of a man in the centre, as well as the words "The Official International Wade Collectors Club" in a black and red printed circle, and the black printed caption "Happy Little Guys." On the bottom of each decanter is printed "Copyright R.Ellis - Ellis Logo Wade"

No.	Description	Colourways	Size	U.S.$	Can.$	U.K.£
1.	Blue "Guy"	White; black chimney hat, facial markings; blue trousers	242	95.00	140.00	70.00
2.	Yellow "Guy"	White; black top hat, facial markings; pink tongue, yellow sweater	242	95.00	140.00	70.00
3.	"Wade"	White; black derby hat, facial markings, bow tie, shoes; pink tongue; red jacket; grey trousers	242	95.00	140.00	70.00

Lockhart Decanter

Five hundred of these decanters were produced.

Lockhart Decatner

Backstamp: Unknown

No.	Description	Colourways	Size	U.S.$	Can.$	U.K.£
1.	Decanter	White; brown/yellow stag print	240	75.00	99.00	45.00

STEINS, 1997

Lockhart Stein

A stein (similar in shape to the "Beethoven" and "Mozart" steins, with a rolled band around the rim and base) was produced for the 27th annual convention. The stein has a transfer print showing the head of a white-tailed stag standing under a tree. The print was taken from an original painting by American wildlife artist James L. Lockhart. There were 305 blue and 361 cream coloured steins available as part of the Wisconsin convention package, but the 224 white steins were sold to clubs only.

Lockhart Stein (No.2)

Backstamp: Unknown

No.	Description	Colourways	Size	U.S.$	Can.$	U.K.£
1.	Stein	Blue; brown/yellow stag print	167	45.00	55.00	30.00
2.	Stein	Cream; brown/yellow stag print	167	45.00	55.00	30.00
3.	Stein	White; brown/yellow stag print	167	45.00	55.00	30.00

Miniature Steins

The miniature tankard in two colours has the "Wade" character printed on the front. It was given as a free gift with the convention package. Four hundred eighty blue and 507 cream tankards were produced.

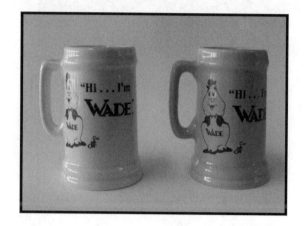

Backstamp: Printed "I.A.J.B.B.S.C. Logo Produced exclusively for I.A.J.B.B.S.C. July 1997 Wade"

No.	Description	Colourways	Size	U.S.$	Can.$	U.K.£
1.	Miniature stein	Blue; dark blue print, lettering "Hi... I'm Wade"	75	20.00	25.00	12.00
2.	Miniature stein	Cream; dark blue print, lettering "Hi... I'm Wade"	75	20.00	25.00	12.00

CONVENTION PRESIDENT'S GIFT, 1997

PLATE

The same cartoon plate in a cream colour was the president's thank-you gift to Chair persons at the convention. A total of 105 plates were produced.

Photograph not available
at press time

Backstamp: Unknown

No.	Description	Colourways	Size	U.S.$	Can.$	u.k.£
1.	Plate	Cream; gold rim; multi-coloured prints; Bottle Collector Cartoon black lettering	260		Unknown	

CLUB AWARDS, 1997

Charity: Water/Whisky Jug, 1997

This water/whisky jug was given to each club that exceeded its charity ticket sales quotas during 1997. The total number of jugs produced was 213.

Backstamp: Printed "Awarded for One Of a Kind Charity Contest Wade England" with the "IAJBBSC" logo and "Wade" between two lines

No.	Description	Colourways	Shape/Size	U.S.$	Can.$	U.K.£
1.	Water/whisky jug	Pale blue; black/red rosette and lettering "Jim Beam Kentucky Straight Bourbon Whiskey"	Square/158		Unknown	

Membership: Christmas Tree Teapot, 1997

A "Christmas Tree Teapot" was given to each club that had maintained or exceeded its previous year6s membership level. Three hundred eighty-two teapots were produced.

Photograph not available
at press time

Backstamp: Printed "Membership Award 1995 I.A.J.B.B.S.C." logo with "Wade" between two lines

No.	Description	Colourways	Shape/Size	U.S.$	Can.$	U.K.£
1.	Teapot	Green; gold star; multi-coloured print	Unknown/146		Unknown	

Membership: Water/Whisky Jug, 1997

A water jug was given to each club that had maIntained or exceeded its previous years membership level. One hundred forty-seven jugs were produced.

Photograph not available
at press time

Backstamp: Printed "Membership Award 1997 I.A.J.B.B.S.C. logo" with "Wade" between two lines

No.	Description	Colourways	Shape/Size	U.S.$	Can.$	U.K.£
1.	Water/Whisky Jug	Yellow; black "I.A.J.B.B.S.C." logo, lettering	Square/158		Unknown	

DISTRICT MEETINGS, 1997

Cartoon Plate

A plate decorated with the Foxy ^{© R.Ellis} logo, Female Fox, *Jo Anne* (the IAJBBSC president), and the Wade Bottle Guy characters and the words "Beam Bottle Collector" was sold at the district meetings held during the Oconomowoc Convention. Three hundred fifty-seven plates were produced.

Backstamp: Printed "Produced Exclusively for the I.A.J.B.B.S.C. July 1997 Copyright 1996 R.Ellis" with "I.A.J.B.B.S.C." logo

No.	Description	Colourways	Size	U.S.$	Can.$	U.K.£
1.	Plate	Yellow; gold rim; multi-coloured prints; Bottle-Collector Cartoon black lettering	260	75.00	90.00	50.00

Foxy © Cookie Jar

The Foxy © cookie jar was available in three colours and in a limited edition of 1,300 (500 cream, 600 blue and 200 white) to Jim Beam Association members who were present at a district meeting during the spring of 1997. The names of the cartoon characters around the jar are Foxy the Fox, Mrs. Foxy, Kangaroo, Canadian Beamer, Beamer of *Deutschland* and the Jim Beam/Wade mascot "Wade".

Backstamp: Black printed "Animated Characters © 1996 R.Ellis," red printed "Wade Porcelain"

No.	Description	Colourways	Size	U.S.$	Can.$	U.K.£
1.	Foxy Cookie Jar	Blue; multi-coloured cartoon characters	266 x 140	75.00	100.00	50.00
2.	Foxy Cookie Jar	Cream; multi-coloured cartoon characters	266 x 140	60.00	75.00	35.00
3.	Foxy Cookie Jar	White; multi-coloured cartoon characters	266 x 140	60.00	75.00	35.00

28TH INTERNATIONAL I.A.J.B.B.S.C. CONVENTION AND THIRD U.S.A. WADE SHOW, BUFFALO, NEW YORK, 1998

COLLECTOR BROOCH AND FIGURE, 1998

Specially produced by Wade for the IAJBBSC were a porcelain brooch in a limited edition of 1,500, and a 1,000 limited edition porcelain model of "Wade," one of the Happy Little Guy characters created by Dick Ellis, cartoonist of the Jim Beam Association. The pin was sold at the IAJBBSC and Wade show for $15.00 US. and the model sold for $50.00 U.S.

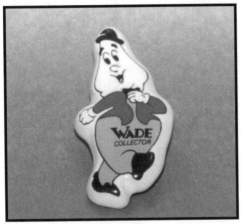

"Brooch"

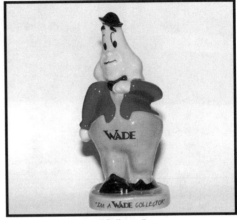

"Collector"

Backstamp: A. Black printed "I.A.J.B.B.S.C. Logo © 1998. R.Ellis" With Ellis signature
B. Black printed "I.A.J.B.B.S.C. Logo & Wade England 1 of 1,000 Animated Characters ©R.Ellis" with Ellis signature

No.	Description	Colourways	Shape/Size	U.S.$	Can.$	U.K.£
1.	Brooch	White, black, dark red and grey Wade character decal; black lettering "Wade Collector"	70	25.00	35.00	25.00
2.	Figure	Black hat, bow tie, shoes; white face, hands; red jacket; grey shirt; trousers and base; black lettering "Wade" "I'm a Wade Collector"	171	65.00	75.00	45.00

DRINK POURERS, 1998

Liquor pourers in two colours were given free with the convention package, but they were also available as individual items. Jim Beam Kentucky Bourbon Straight Whiskey was printed on 500 and on the other 500 was printed Jim Beam. The pourers cost $20.00 each.

Drink Pourer No.1 (Left); No.3 (Right)

Backstamp: A. Impressed "C57" on underside of button
B. Red printed "Wade" impressed "C57 Made in England"

No.	Description	Colourways	Shape/Size	U.S.$	Can.$	U.K.£
1.	Drink Pourer	White; metal spout, neck; red rosette; black/yellow/red lettering "Jim Beam Kentucky Straight Bourbon Whiskey"	C57/29 x 60 Rectangular	30.00	38.00	15.00
2.	Drink Pourer	Yellow; metal spout, neck; red rosette; black lettering "Jim Beam Kentucky Straight Bourbon Whiskey"	C57/29 x 60 Rectangular	25.00	30.00	15.00
3.	Drink Pourer	White; metal spout, neck; red rosette; black/yellow lettering "Jim Beam"	C57/29 x 60 Rectangular	25.00	30.00	15.00

WATER/WHISKY JUG, 1998

This jug was produced in three colours and has a transfer print on the front of a North American bison. The print was taken from an original painting by American Wildlife artist James L. Lockhart. The jug was part of the convention package, but others were sold at the convention for $40.00 each. Three hundred and seven green jugs, and 405 cream jugs were produced. One hundred ninety-seven white jugs were produced and sold to clubs only as special items for club raffles.

Backstamp: Printed "Genuine Wade Porcelain"

No.	Description	Colourways	Shape/Size	U.S.$	Can.$	U.K.£
1.	Jug Lockhart Bison	Cream; brown/yellow print	Unknown	45.00	60.00	30.00
2.	Jug Lockhart Bison	Green; brown/yellow print	Unknown	45.00	60.00	30.00
3.	Jug Lockhart Bison	White; brown/yellow print	Unknown	45.00	60.00	30.00

PRESIDENT'S GIFT, 1998

A pink cartoon "Beam Around The World" plate in a limited edition of 113 was the president's gift to committee chair members for 1998.

Backstamp: Printed "I.A.J.B.B.S.C. (Logo) Wade Animated Characters © 1998 R. Ellis" with Ellis signature and wording "Thanks for your support Buffalo 1998" signed Jo-Anne

No.	Description	Colourways	Shape/Size	U.S.$	Can.$	U.K.£
1.	Plate	Pink; gold rim; multi-coloured prints; black lettering "Beam Around the World"	260		Unknown	

CLUB AWARDS, 1998

Charity: Water/Whisky Jug, 1998

This water/whisky jug was was given to each club that exceeded its charity ticket sales quotas during 1997. The charity drive jugs are never sold.

Photograph not available
at press time

Backstamp: Unknown

No.	Description	Colourways	Size	U.S.$	Can.$	U.K.£
1.	Water/Whisky Jug	Cream; black rosette, lettering "Kentucky Straight Bourbon Whiskey"	Square/158		Unknown	

Membership: Water/Whisky Jug, 1998

A water jug was given to each club that had maintained or exceeded its previous years membership level. One hundred fifty-six jugs were produced.

Photograph not available
at press time

Backstamp: Printed "1998 Membership Award I.A.J.B.B.S.C. Wade"

No.	Description	Colourways	Size	U.S.$	Can.$	U.K.£
1.	Water/Whisky Jug	Dark blue; black rosette, lettering "Jim Beam Kentucky Straight Bourbon Whiskey"	Unknown		Unknown	

DISTRICT MEETINGS, 1998

Cartoon Plate

A green cartoon "Beam Around The World" plate was sold at the district meetings held during the 27th International IAJBBSC Convention and third U.S.A. Wade show, Buffalo, New York, July 1998. Total number of plates produced was 386.

Backstamp: Printed "I.A.J.B.B.S.C. (Logo) Wade Animated Characters © 1998 R. Ellis" and signed Ellis

No.	Description	Colourways	Shape/Size	U.S.$	Can.$	U.K.£
1.	Plate	Green; gold rim; multi-coloured prints; black lettering "Beam Around the World"	260		Unknown	

Cream Jug and Sugar Bowl

There were a total of 1,374 sets of the "Foxy and Characters" milk jug and sugar bowl produced in three colours. Each colour was in a limited edition: 636 sets in blue glaze; 504 sets in cream glaze; 234 sets in white glaze. The blue and cream sets were originally sold at IAJBBSC spring district meetings, and others were sold at the convention. The cost of each set at the show was $40.00 U.S.

Backstamp: Printed "Animated Characters © 1997 R. Ellis Genuine Wade Porcelain" with Ellis Foxy © logo

No.	Description	Colourways	Shape/Size	U.S.$	Can.$	U.K.£
1.	Jug/Bowl	Blue; multi-coloured prints (Pair)	Round/95/65	40.00	45.00	20.00
2.	Jug/Bowl	Cream; multi-coloured prints (Pair)	Round/95/65	40.00	45.00	20.00
3.	Jug/Bowl	White; multi-coloured prints (Pair)	Round/95/65	45.00	50.00	25.00

29TH INTERNATIONAL I.A.J.B.B.S.C. CONVENTION AND
3RD U.S.A. WADE SHOW, SAN ANTONIO, TEXAS, 1999

DECANTERS

A decanter in the shape of a "Rodeo Cowboy Trophy Buckle" was produced for members of the IAJBBSC and Wade Collectors attending the convention who purchased the $160.00 convention package. There were two versions of the decanter produced: one for ladies and one for men. Only 300 of each were produced.

Backstamp: Printed "I.A.J.B.B.S.C 1999 © 1998 R.Ellis Wade 29th Annual Convention San Antonio, Texas 1 of 300"

No.	Description	Colourways	Shape/Size	U.S.$	Can.$	U.K.£
1.	Jim Beam Sour Mash	Black hat, shirt; yellow hair; brown boots; Beams Sour Mash belt buckle; white base	165		Unknown	
2.	Jim Beam Whisky	Brown hat, boots; yellow hair; red shirt; Jim Beam belt buckle; white base	165		Unknown	

DRINK POURERS

The "Rodeo Cowboy Trophy Buckle" liquor pourers were produced in two colours and in a limited edition of 450 of each colour.

Photograph not available
at press time

Backstamp: Unknown

No.	Description	Colourways	Size	U.S.$	Can.$	u.k.£
1.	Drink Pourer	Unknown	Unknown		Unknown	
2.	Drink Pourer	Unknown	Unknown		Unknown	

FIGURE

Texas Fox

A model of a Fox was sold at the San Antonio, Texas, IAJBBSC convention issued in a limited edition of 160 models. Eighty of the models were sold on Saturday July 10 and eighty on Sunday July11th. The original cost of the Texas Fox was $40.00 U.S.

Backstamp: Printed "I.A.J.B.B.S.C 1999 © 1998 R.Ellis Wade San Antonio, Texas 1 of 160"

No.	Description	Colourways	Size	U.S.$	Can.$	U.K.£
1.	Texas Fox figure	Black hat/white band; red coat; white trousers; yellow Lone Star State flag plaque; brown base	102	40.00	55.00	25.00

VASES

A special bud vase with a print of an eagle on the front from an original painting by famous American Wildlife artist James Lockhart was produced in two colours and in a limited edition of one hundred and fifty and was sold at the July 1999 convention for 35.00 (U.S.) each.

Photograph not available
at press time

Backstamp: Unknown

No.	Description	Colourways	Size	U.S.$	Can.$	U.K.£
1.	Vase	White; multi-coloured print	Unknown	35.00	45.00	20.00
2.	Vase	Pale yellow; multi-coloured print	Unknown	35.00	45.00	20.00

WHISKY JUG

These whisky jugs were produced in two-tone colours in limiteds edition of 300 brown and almond, and 300 dark and light blue. They are decorated with a print of a cowboy leaning on a large whisky bottle and holding a glass. Original cost was $35.00 U.S.

Backstamp: Printed "I.A.J.B.B.S.C. 1999 Wade 1 of 300"

No.	Description	Colourways	Size	U.S.$	Can.$	U.K.£
1.	Whisky Jug	Brown/tan; multi-coloured print	215	35.00	45.00	20.00
2.	Whisky Jug	Dark blue/light blue; multi coloured print	215	35.00	45.00	20.00

CLUBS AWARDS

Fox Membership Figure

In 1999 Jim Beam introduced their first Wade membership model of a Fox (which is the Jim Beam Mascot). The Fox, wearing a green coat and holding a plaque with the IAJBBSC logo printed on it, was designed by Richard Ellis and could be ordered by new and renewing members who sent in their membership fees before April 15th 1999. At the April 15th deadline a count would be made of the orders and only that amount of models would be made by Wade Ceramics. The original cost direct from IAJBBSC was $28.00 (U.S.). A second Fox model wearing a red coat was available at the IAJBBSC convention, this model holds a plaque with the Lone Star State Flag of Texas printed on it (see page 161).

Backstamp: Printed "I.A.J.B.B.S.C 1999 © 1998 R.Ellis Wade San Antonio, Texas 1 of "

No.	Description	Colourways	Shape/Size	U.S.$	Can.$	U.K.£
1.	Fox Figure	Black hat/white band; green coat; white trousers; blue IAJBBSC plaque; brown base	102	40.00	50.00	25.00

Gold Membership Fox Figure

A "Name the Fox" contest was organized by the IAJBBSC. Members could submit five names by the April first deadline: from the selection one name would be chosen by the committee and the submitting member would win the all-over one of a kind gold membership Fox.

Photograph not available
at press time

Backstamp: Printed "I.A.J.B.B.S.C 1999 © 1998 R.Ellis Wade San Antonio, Texas"

No.	Description	Colourways	Shape/Size	U.S.$	Can.$	U.K.£
1.	Gold Fox	Fox/Gold	102		Unique	

DISTRICT MEETINGS, 1999

At the IAJBBSC spring district meetings an "Old Crow" water jug was available to attending members who bought a full package. It was produced in three colours: 200 black, 500 burgundy, and 600 yellow. Odd-numbered districts had the yellow jug, and even-numbered districts had the burgundy jug. The black jugs were for special use by the IAJBBSC. The original cost was $25.00 U.S. each.

Backstamp: **A.** Printed "I.A.J.B.B.S.C. 1999 Wade 1 of 200"
B. Printed "I.A.J.B.B.S.C. 1999 Wade 1 of 500"
C. Printed "I.A.J.B.B.S.C. 1999 Wade 1 of 600"

No.	Description	Colourways	Size	U.S.$	Can.$	U.K.£
1.	Water Jug	Black; white label; black crow print/lettering "Old Crow Since 1835 The Original Sour Mash Kentucky Straight Bourbon Whiskey"	Rectangular/171		Unknown	
2.	Water Jug	Burgundy; white label; black crow print/lettering "Old Crow Since 1835 The Original Sour Mash Kentucky Straight Bourbon Whiskey"	Rectangular/171		Unknown	
3.	Water Jug	Yellow; white label; black crow print/lettering "Old Crow Since 1835 The Original Sour Mash Kentucky Straight Bourbon Whiskey"	Rectangular/171		Unknown	

INVER HOUSE GREEN PLAID RARE SCOTCH WHISKY

ASHTRAY

Backstamp: Printed "Wade pdm Made in England" within two red lines (p d m separate 1990-1996)

No.	Description	Colourways	Shape/Size	U.S.$	Can.$	U.K.£
1.	Ashtray	White; green tartan band; dark green lettering "Inver House Green Plaid Rare Scotch Whisky"	Square/130	12.00	15.00	8.00

IRISH MIST WHISKEY BASED LIQUEUR
IRISH MIST LIQUEUR COMPANY

DECANTER AND DRINK POURER, 1970-1975

Backstamp: **A.** Embossed "This is a fine piece of Irish Porcelain made by Wade Liqueur Bottle Tullamore, Ireland"
B. Impressed "5455/1" on underside of button

No.	Description	Colourways	Size	U.S.$	Can.$	U.K.£
1.	Decanter	Blue; multi-coloured label, lettering "Irish Mist Liqueur"	225	50.00	70.00	25.00
2.	Drink Pourer	White; plastic spout, neck; blue lettering "Irish Mist" Octagonal/40 x 47		25.00	30.00	10.00

ISLE OF JURA DISTILLERY CO. LTD.

WATER JUG

This heavy stone-coloured water jug has a print of Scottish hills on the front and has no handle.

Backstamp: None

No.	Description	Colourways	Size	U.S.$	Can.$	U.K.£
1.	Water jug	Mottled stone; dark brown print, lettering "Isle of Jura Pure Malt Whisky guaranteed 8 years old"	Round/177	35.00	40.00	18.00

J & B SCOTCH WHISKY

ASHTRAYS, 1955-1984

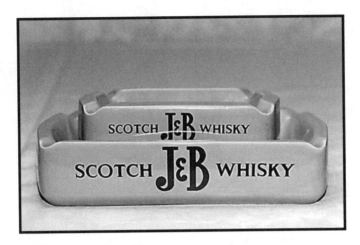

Backstamp: A. "Wade Regicor, London England," laurel leaves, large size
B. "Wade pdm England"

No.	Description	Colourways	Size	U.S.$	Can.$	U.K.£
1.	Small	Cream; black/red lettering "Scotch J & B Whisky"	Rectangular/153	10.00	15.00	5.00
2.	Large	Cream; black/red lettering "Scotch J & B Whisky"	Rectangular/216	15.00	20.00	8.00

DRINK POURERS

Drink Pourer (No. 1)

Drink Pourer (No. 4)

Backstamp: "Reginald Corfield Limited Redhill Surrey," "Wade Regicor England"

No.	Description	Colourways	Size	U.S.$	Can.$	U.K.£
1.	Drink Pourer	Cream; metal tube, spout; red lettering "J & B"	Circular C53/41	30.00	35.00	15.00
2.	Drink Pourer	Green; plastic tube; red lettering "J & B"	Circular C53/41	30.00	35.00	15.00

DRINK POURERS

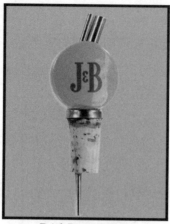

Drink Pourer (No.3)

Drink Pourer (No.5)

No.	Description	Colourways	Size	U.S.$	Can.$	U.K.£
3.	Drink Pourer	Lime green; metal spout, neck; red lettering "J & B"	Round C53/41 x 44	20.00	25.00	10.00
4.	Drink Pourer	White/lime green; plastic spout, neck; red lettering"J & B"	Round C53/41 x 44	30.00	38.00	12.00
5.	Drink Pourer	Black; metal spout, neck; red/gold lettering "J & B Rare Scotch Whisky"	Round C53/41 x 44	30.00	38.00	12.00

WATER JUG, 1968-1984

No.	Description	Colourways	Size	U.S.$	Can.$	U.K.£
1.	Water Jug	Dull yellow; red/black lettering "J & B Scotch Whisky"	Rectangular/153	28.00	32.00	20.00

JACK DANIEL'S WHISKY

DRINK POURERS, 1990-1996

The octagonal pourer is shape number 5455/1. The square pourer, shape number C52A, has a notched base and shoulders.

Photograph not available
at press time

Backstamp: Unmarked

No.	Description	Colourways	Shape/Size	U.S.$	Can.$	U.K.£
1.	Drink Pourer	Black; plastic tube; white lettering "Jack Daniel's"	Octagonal/40	30.00	35.00	15.00
2.	Drink Pourer	Black; plastic tube; white lettering "Jack Daniel's Old No 7"	Square/38	30.00	35.00	15.00

JAMES GILBERT LTD

DECANTER, 1995

A limited edition of 250 ceramic rugby-ball shaped decanters were manufactured by Wade Ceramics for James Gilbert Ltd. to commemorate the Rugby World Cup in 1995. The original cost of the decanter was £19.99.

Backstamp: Printed "Genuine Wade Porcelain"

No.	Description	Colourways	Size	U.S.$	Can.$	U.K.£
1.	Decanter	White/blue; black lettering "Gilbert Maker Rubgy"	200	65.00	90.00	45.00

JAMES MARTIN'S V.V.O. SCOTCH WHISKY

WATER JUGS

Water Jug (No.1)

Backstamp: A. Printed circular "Reginald Corfield Limited, Redhill Surrey," with "Regicor Wade England" through the circle (1968-1969)
B. Printed "Wade pdm" (pdm joined 1969-1984)

No.	Description	Colourways	Shape/Size	U.S.$	Can.$	U.K.£
1.	Water Jug	Black; white panel; red/yellow lettering "Martin's V.V.O. Grown Up Scotch Years 8 Old"	Rectangular/147	35.00	40.00	18.00
2.	Water Jug	Black; red lettering "James Martin's V.V.O. Blended Scotch Whisky"	Round/177	35.00	40.00	18.00

JAMESON IRISH WHISKEY
JOHN JAMESON & SON

ASHTRAY, DECANTER AND DRINK POURER, 1982-1990

The ashtray was produced between 1984 and 1990, the decanter between 1982 and 1986.

 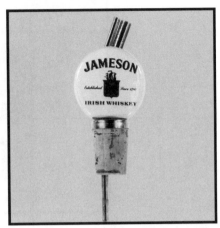

Backstamp: A. "Wade p d m England"
B. Green circular transfer printed "Made in Ireland—Porcelain Wade—eire tire a dheanta" with a shamrock and crown in the centre

No.	Description	Colourways	Shape/Size	U.S.$	Can.$	U.K.£
1.	Ashtray	Cream; black/red/yellow lettering "Jameson Irish Whiskey"	Round/216	10.00	15.00	5.00
2.	Decanter	White; green shamrocks, gold lettering "Jameson Irish Whiskey"	235	50.00	70.00	25.00
3.	Drink Pourer	Cream; metal spout, neck; black lettering "Jameson Established Since 1780 Irish Whiskey"	C53/41 x 44 Round	30.00	35.00	120.00

JAMIE STUART SCOTCH WHISKY

WATER JUG

The water jug has an ice check spout.

Backstamp: Printed "Wade Regicor London England," in a laurel leaf frame (large size 18 x 20 mm 1953-1962)

No.	Description	Colourways	Shape/Size	U.S.$	Can.$	U.K.£
1.	Water Jug	Yellow; red crest; red/black lettering "Jamie Stuart Scotch Whisky"	Rectangular/135	30.00	35.00	15.00

JANEIRO

DRINK POURER

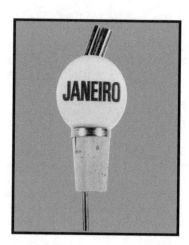

Backstamp: None

No.	Description	Colourways	Shape/Size	U.S.$	Can.$	U.K.£
1.	Drink Pourer	White; metal spout, neck; dark green lettering "Janeiro"	Round C53/41 x 44	25.00	38.00	10.00

JOHN BEGG SCOTCH WHISKY

ASHTRAY, DRINK POURERS AND WATER JUGS, 1955-1984

The water jugs have open spouts. The pourers are shape number C53.

Ashtray "John Begg Scotch whisky"

Water Jug "Take a Peg of John Begg"

Drink Pourer (No.2)

Drink Pourer (No.3)

Backstamp: A. "Wade Regicor, London England," laurel leaves, large size
B. "Reginald Corfield Limited Redhill Surrey," "Wade Regicor England"
C. "Wade pdm England"

No.	Description	Colourways	Shape/Size	U.S.$	Can.$	U.K.£
1.	Ashtray	Blue; white lettering "John Begg Scotch Whisky"	Triangular/153	15.00	20.00	8.00
2.	Drink Pourer	White/blue; metal spout, tube; white lettering (front) "Take and Peg of John Begg" (back) "John Begg Scotch Whisky"	Round/41 x 44	18.00	25.00	12.00
3.	Drink Pourer	White/blue; metal spout, tube; white lettering "John Begg"	Round/41 x 44	18.00	25.00	12.00
4.	Water Jug	Dark blue; white lettering "John Begg Scotch Whisky"	Square/127	30.00	35.00	15.00
5.	Water Jug	White; dark blue lettering "Take a Peg of John Begg!"	Square/127	30.00	35.00	15.00

JOHN BULL BITTER

ASHTRAYS, 1969-1990

The print on style No. 1 is of the brewery gates. A print of John Bull is on No. 2 and 3.

Photograph not available
at press time

Backstamp: A. "Wade pdm England"
B. "Wade P D M England"

No.	Description	Colourways	Shape/Size	U.S.$	Can.$	U.K.£
1.	Ashtray	Cream; black print; black/red lettering "John Bull Bitter"	Round/165	10.00	15.00	5.00
2.	Ashtray	Cream; black/red print, lettering "John Bull Bitter"	Triangular/177	25.00	30.00	12.00
3.	Ashtray	Yellow; black/red print, lettering "John Bull Bitter"	Triangular/177	25.00	30.00	12.00

JOHN COURAGE

ASHTRAY, 1969-1984

The print on this ashtray is a silhouette of the head of John Courage.

Backstamp: "Wade pdm England"

No.	Description	Colourways	Shape/Size	U.S.$	Can.$	U.K.£
1.	Ashtray	Black; black print; yellow/white lettering "John Courage IPA"	Round/230	12.00	16.00	8.00

JOHN SMITH BREWERY

PUMP HANDLE, c.1980

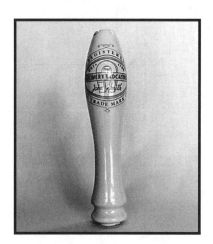

Backstamp: Unmarked

No.	Description	Colourways	Size	U.S.$	Can.$	U.K.£
1.	Pump Handle	Off white; green print, lettering "Registered Trade Mark Estd. 1758. The John Smith Brewery Tadcaster"	225	30.00	35.00	15.00

JOHNNIE WALKER SCOTCH WHISKY
UNITED DISTILLERS UK PLC

ASHTRAYS, 1955-1996

Ashtray (No.1)

Ashtray (No.2)

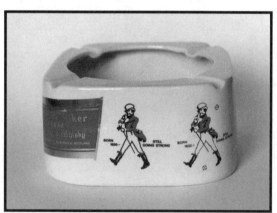

Ashtray (No.10)

Ashtray (No.11)

Backstamp: **A.** "Wade Regicor, London England," laurel leaves, large size
                   B. "Wade pdm England"
                   C. "Wade p d m England"
                   D. "Wade P D M Made in England"
                   E. Printed circular "Wade pdm" (pdm joined 1969-1984)

No.	Description	Colourways	Shape/Size	U.S.$	Can.$	U.K.£
1.	Ashtray	Pale blue; multi-coloured print; black lettering "Born 1820 - Still Going Strong"	Oval/260	15.00	20.00	8.00
2.	Ashtray	Pale blue; multi-coloured print; black lettering "Born 1820 - Still Going Strong"	Rectangular/225	15.00	20.00	8.00
3.	Ashtray	White; multi-coloured print, red lettering "Johnnie Walker Scotch Whisky"	Square/120	25.00	30.00	12.00
4.	Ashtray	White; multi-coloured print, red lettering "Johnnie Walker"	Square/127	25.00	30.00	12.00
5.	Ashtray	Cream; red/black lettering "Johnnie Walker"	Square/127	15.00	20.00	8.00
6.	Ashtray	Light blue; multi-coloured print; black lettering "Johnnie Walker"	Square/159	10.00	15.00	5.00
7.	Ashtray	Light blue; multi-coloured print, black lettering "Johnnie Walker"	Square/165	10.00	15.00	5.00
8.	Ashtray	White/red; gold lettering "Johnnie Walker England Old Scotch Whisky"	Square/171	10.00	15.00	5.00
9.	Ashtray	Black; red/gold lettering "Johnnie Walker Black Label"	Square/159	10.00	15.00	5.00
10.	Ashtray	White; red/gold label; red/black prints; black lettering "Born 1820 Still Going Strong"	Cube/127	12.00	18.00	9.00
11.	Ashtray	Pale blue; multi-coloured print; black lettering "Born 1820 Still Going Strong"	Square/120	12.00	18.00	9.00

DRINK POURERS, 1960-1970

The drink pourers were issued between 1960 and 1970. The style No. 1 drink pourer is shape number C53, with a straight base and a dust flap at the end of the metal tube. Style No. 2 is shape number 5455/4.

Drink Pourer (No.1)

Drink Pourer (No.4)

Drink Pourer (No.5)

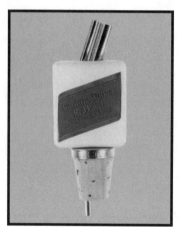
Drink Pourer (No.6)

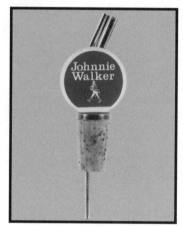
Drink Pourer (No.7)

Backstamp: **A.** "Wade Regicor, London England," laurel leaves, large size
B. "Wade Regicor, London England," laurel leaves, small size
C. "Reginald Corfield Limited Redhill Surrey," "Wade Regicor England"
D. "Fine Staffordshire Pottery Duncan Fox & Co, Inc, New York - Regicor, Wade England"
E. Printed circular "Wade pdm" (pdm joined 1969-1984)

No.	Description	Colourways	Shape/Size	U.S.$	Can.$	U.K.£
1.	Drink Pourer	White; metal tube, spout, flap; red/black lettering "Johnnie Walker Scotch Whisky Born 1820 - Still Going Strong"	Circular/41	30.00	35.00	15.00
2.	Drink Pourer	Black; metal tube; gold lettering "Johnnie Walker Black Label"	Rectangular/46	30.00	35.00	15.00
3.	Drink Pourer	White; metal tube; red/gold lettering "Johnnie Walker"	Rectangular/46	30.00	35.00	15.00
4.	Drink Pourer	White; metal spout, tube, flap; red/black lettering "Johnnie Walker Born 1820 Still Going Strong Scotch Whisky"	C53/41 x 44 Round	28.00	35.00	15.00
5.	Drink Pourer	White/red; plastic spout, tube; white print/lettering "Johnnie Walker"	C53A/40 x 44 Round	28.00	35.00	15.00
6.	Drink Pourer	White/red; metal spout, neck; gold lettering "Johnnie Walker Red Label Old Scotch Whisky"	C62/47 x 41 Rectangular	15.00	20.00	10.00
7.	Drink Pourer	White/red; metal spout, tube; white print/lettering "Johnny Walker"	C53A/41 x 44 Round	28.00	35.00	15.00

WATER JUGS, 1955-1996

Water Jug (No.1)

Water Jug (No.2)

Water Jug (No.5)

Water Jug (No.6)

Water Jug (No.7)

Backstamp: **A.** "Wade Regicor, London England," laurel leaves, large size
B. "Wade Regicor, London England," laurel leaves, small size
C. "Reginald Corfield Limited Redhill Surrey," "Wade Regicor England"
D. "Fine Staffordshire Pottery Duncan Fox & Co, Inc, New York - Regicor, Wade England"
E. Gold printed "Wade pdm" (pdm joined 1969-1984)

No.	Description	Colourways	Shape/Size	U.S.$	Can.$	U.K.£
1.	Water Jug, ice-check spout	Pale blue; multi-coloured print, black lettering "Johnnie Walker Born 1820 - Still Going Strong"	Round/133	35.00	40.00	22.00
2.	Water Jug, open spout	"Johnnie Walker Red Label"				
3.	Water Jug, ice-check spout	White; red/black print, lettering "Johnnie Walker Scotch Whisky"	Square/146	35.00	40.00	22.00
4.	Water Jug, open spout	Red/white/black print, lettering "Johnnie Walker"	Square/160	35.00	40.00	22.00
5.	Water Jug	Black; gold lettering "Johnnie Walker Black Label Scotch Years 12 Old" in gold wreath	Round/195	35.00	40.00	22.00
6.	Water Jug	Black; gold lettering "Johnnie Walker 12 Years old Black Label Scotch" in gold frame	Round/190	30.00	35.00	22.00
7.	Water Jug, open spout	Pale blue; multi-coloured Johnnie Walker print; black lettering "Born 1820 Still Going Strong"	Rectangular/160	35.00	40.00	22.00

JOSE CUERVO

DRINK POURER

Backstamp: None

No.	Description	Colourways	Shape/Size	U.S.$	Can.$	U.K.£
1.	Drink Pourer	White/black panel; plastic spout, neck lettering "Jose Cuervo"	C54/37 x 60 Rectangular	25.00	30.00	10.00

IF YOU WANT ALICE
YOU MUST JOIN THE

"CLUB"

THE OFFICIAL
INTERNATIONAL WADE
COLLECTOR'S CLUB

Membership offers, besides the pleasure of sharing a hobby, such intangibles as greater appreciation of Wade collectables through initiation into techniques of designing, modelling and production. You can find out about inspired ideas that led to the creation of a new series of figurines — all ready to charm and capture the heart.

• ANNUAL MEMBERSHIP FIGURE

New each year, these exclusive annual membership figures become collector's items in their own right. "Alice" is the membership model for the 1999 year.

• MEMBERSHIP CERTIFICATE

Every new member receives a personalized membership certificate on joining.

• *WADE'S WORLD* MAGAZINE

This quarterly full-colour club magazine is packed with information on limited editions, club news, Wade fairs and events, and Wanted and For Sale adverts.

• CLUB LIMITED EDITIONS

Only club members can participate in purchasing the various club limited edition figures which are offered every year.

• ANNUAL MEMBERSHIP PIN

Each year a new collector's pin is included free with membership. The 1998 collector's pin was "The Wade Baby."

In the U.K.
Royal Works, Westport Road, Burslem
Stoke-on-Trent, ST6 4AP England
Tel.: 01782 255255 Fax.: 01782 575195
E-mail: club@wade.co.uk

In the U.S.
O.I.W.C.C.
3330 Cobb Parkway, Suite 17-333,
Acworth, Georgia 30101, USA
Tel.: 770 529 9908 Fax.: 770 529 1515

http://www.wade.co.uk/wade

MEMBERSHIP OPTIONS

ANNUAL INDIVIDUAL MEMBERSHIP

(12 months from receipt of application)
UK Membership £20
Overseas Membership £25 or US $42

ANNUAL FAMILY MEMBERSHIP

(12 months from receipt of application)
UK Membership £68
Overseas Membership £82 or US $144

A family of four can enjoy full membership benefits. This is offered for up to four people; any additional family members will be charged at the full rate no reduction for families of less than four. All family membership's must enrol on one application form and all membership's will commence from the same month.

TWO-YEAR MEMBERSHIP

(24 months from receipt of application)
UK Membership £36
Overseas Membership £46 or US $78

Receive a special bonus price when you join for two years. You will receive your current years membership piece on receipt of your application and on the anniversary of your membership, you will automatically receive your second piece.

ENROL A FRIEND

The "Enrol a Friend" scheme is available when you introduce a new member for a one-year membership. Your friend will enjoy all the benefits of club membership plus you will both be sent a BONUS GIFT.

MEMBERSHIP APPLICATION FORM

Please enrol me/my family/my friend as a member(s):

Title . . . . First Name . . . . . Last Name . . . .
Address . . . .
. . . .
Post/Zip Code . . . . Telephone Number . . . .
❑My cheque for . . . . made to payable to Wade Ceramics Limited is enclosed (cheques are accepted in pounds sterling and US dollars)
❑ Debit my credit/charge card ❑ Visa ❑Access ❑American Express for the sum of . . .
Card No. ❑❑❑❑❑❑❑❑❑❑❑❑❑❑❑❑ Expiry ❑❑❑❑
Other 3 Family Names (for family membership): . . . .

Enrol a Friend and Both Receive a Bonus Gift

Title . . . . . First Name . . . . Last Name . . . .
Address . . . .
. . . .
Postal/Zip Code . . . . Telephone Number . . . .
My Membership Number . . . .
Friend's Signature . . . . Date . . . .
I am/am not a member of the Jim Beam Bottle Club . . . . Number . . . .

Send to:
THE OFFICIAL INTERNATIONAL WADE COLLECTORS CLUB

Wade Ceramics Limited
Royal Works, Westport Road, Burslem,
Stoke-on-Trent, ST6 4AP **England**
Tel.: 01782 255255 Fax.: 01782 575195
E-mail: club@wade.co.uk   http://www.wade.co.uk/wade

O.I.W.C.C.
3330 Cobb Parkway, Suite 17-333,
Acworth, Georgia 30101, **USA**
Tel.: 770 529 9908 Fax.: 770 529 1515

JUBILEE STOUT

ASHTRAY, CRUET AND WATER JUG, 1955-1984

The ashtray and cruets were produced between 1955 and 1962, the water jug between 1969 and 1984. The mustard pot is the same shape as the salt and pepper, with the addition of a lid. The water jug has an open spout.

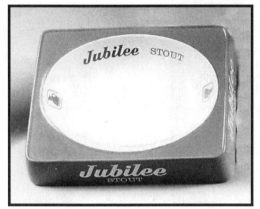

Ashtray

Water Jug

Backstamp: A. "Wade Regicor, London England," laurel leaves, large size
B. "Wade pdm England"

No.	Description	Colourways	Shape/Size	U.S.$	Can.$	U.K.£
1.	Ashtray	Dark blue/white; blue lettering "Jubilee Stout"	Rectangular/210	10.00	15.00	5.00
2.	Mustard Pot	White; blue/red lettering "Jubilee Stout Mustard"	Square/76	8.00	10.00	3.00
3.	Pepper Pot	White; blue/red lettering "Jubilee Stout Pepper"	Square/80	8.00	10.00	3.00
4.	Salt Cellar	White; blue/red lettering "Jubilee Stout Salt"	Square/80	8.00	10.00	3.00
5.	Water Jug	White; red/blue label lettering "Jubilee Stout"	Square/120	25.00	30.00	12.00

KENTUCKY TAVERN BOURBON

WATER JUG, 1968-1969

This jug has a recessed handle and an open spout.

Backstamp: "Reginald Corfield Limited Redhill Surrey," "Wade Regicor England, KY. Straight Bourbon Whisky 86 and 100 Bottled in Bond Glenmore Distilleries Co. Louisville, Owensbord K.Y."

No.	Description	Colourways	Shape/Size	U.S.$	Can.$	U.K.£
1.	Water Jug	White; black/red lettering "8 Year Old Kentucky Tavern The Vintage Bourbon"	Round/190	30.00	35.00	15.00

KING GEORGE SCOTCH WHISKY

ASHTRAYS, 1955-1962

The ashtrays were produced between 1955 and 1962. Each is decorated with a print of King George IV.

Ashtray (No.2)

Backstamp: A. "Wade Regicor, London England," laurel leaves, large size
B. "Wade Regicor, London England," laurel leaves, small size
C. Printed "Wade Regicor Made in England" in laurel leaf frame (small size 13 x 13 mm 1962-late 1968) on neck

No.	Description	Colourways	Shape/Size	U.S.$	Can.$	U.K.£
1.	Ashtray	Creamy yellow; multi-coloured print; red/black lettering "King George IV Scotch Whisky"	Square/108	10.00	15.00	5.00
2.	Ashtray	Pale yellow; blue/red lettering "King George IV Old Scotch Whisky"	Rectangular/55 x 105	10.00	12.00	6.00

184

DRINK POURERS

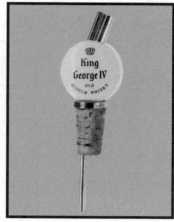

Drink Pourer (No.1)   Drink Pourer (No.2)   Drink Pourer (No.3)

Backstamp: None

No.	Description	Colourways	Shape/Size	U.S.$	Can.$	U.K.£
1.	Drink Pourer	White/yellow; metal spout, tube; multi-coloured print; blue lettering; (front) "King George IV Old Scotch Whisky" and portrait ; (back) portrait only	C53/41 x 44 Round	35.00	45.00	20.00
2.	Drink Pourer	White/yellow; metal spout, tube, dust flap; (front) multi-coloured portrait; (back) blue lettering "King George IV Old Scotch Whisky"	C53/41 x 44 Round	35.00	45.00	20.00
3.	Drink Pourer	White/yellow; metal spout,tube; brown/blue lettering, (front) "King George IV Old Scotch Whisky;" Crown; (back) portrait only	C53/41 x 44 Round	30.00	35.00	12.00

WATER JUGS, 1955-1968

Jug No. 1 has a recessed handle.

Water Jug (No.3)

Water Jug (No.4)

Water Jug (No.5)

Water Jug (No.6)

Backstamp: A. Printed "Wade Regicor Made in England" in laurel leaf frame (small size 13 x 13mm 1962-late 1968) on neck
B. Printed "Wade pdm" (pdm joined 1969-1984)
C. Printed "Wade pdm England" (pdm separated 1984-1990)

No.	Description	Colourways	Shape/Size	U.S.$	Can.$	U.K.£
1.	Water Jug, open spout	Black; gold print, lettering "King George Old Scotch Whisky"	Round/120	30.00	35.00	15.00
2.	Water Jug, ice-check spout	Yellow; multi-coloured print; red/black lettering "King George Old Scotch Whisky"	Round/114	30.00	35.00	15.00
3.	Water Jug, open spout	Yellow; multi-coloured print; black/red lettering "King George Old Scotch Whisky"	Square/114	30.00	35.00	15.00
4.	Water Jug	Black; gold portrait print and lettering "King George IV Blended Scotch Whisky"	Round/114	35.00	45.00	18.00
5.	Water Jug	White; multi-coloured portrait; blue lettering "King George IV Old Scotch Whisky"	Square/114	35.00	45.00	18.00
6.	Water Jug	White; multi-coloured print of Scotsman and man; black lettering "Say When Man" and "King George IV Scotch Whiskey"	Round/118	35.00	40.00	18.00

KING OF KINGS
JAMES MUNROE & SON LTD

ASHTRAYS

Backstamp: **A.** Circular transfer printed "Reginald Corfield Ltd Redhill Surrey -Wade Regicor England" (late 1968- late 1969)
B. Printed "Wade pdm" (pdm joined 1969-1984)

No.	Description	Colourways	Shape/Size	U.S.$	Can.$	U.K.£
1.	Ashtray	Amber; red lettering "King of Kings Rare Old De Luxe Scotch Whisky"	Oval/153	10.00	12.00	5.00
2.	Ashtray	Amber; red lettering, "King of Kings Rare Old De Luxe Scotch Whisky"	Oval/159	10.00	12.00	5.00

KING OF SCOTS
DOUGLAS LAING & CO. LTD. GLASGOW

WATER JUG

This square-shaped jug has a small open spout.

Photograph not available
at press time

Backstamp: Printed "Wade pdm England" (pdm joined 1969-1984)

No.	Description	Colourways	Shape/Size	U.S.$	Can.$	U.K.£
1.	Water Jug	Black; white print, lettering "King of Scots Finest Scotch Whisky Douglas Laing & Co Ltd Glasgow"	Square/114	35.00	40.00	20.00

KINGSFORD'S WHISKY LTD

DECANTER, c.1988

On the front of this Irish Wade decanter is a transfer print of mounted fox hunters.

Photograph not available
at press time

Backstamp: "Wade Ireland"

No.	Description	Colourways	Size	U.S.$	Can.$	U.K.£
1.	Decanter	White; multi-coloured print; black lettering "Kingsford's" Decanter	175	50.00	70.00	25.00

KINGS PRIVILEGE
BRUCE & COMPANY (LEITH) LTD

DECANTER

Backstamp: Gold printed "Genuine Wade Porcelain"

No.	Description	Colourways	Shape/Size	U.S.$	Can.$	U.K.£
1.	Decanter	Black; gold decoration, lettering "Year 21 Old Kings Privilege Scotch Whisky Distilled Blended & Bottled in Scotland Bruce & Company (Leith) Ltd"	Round/203	22.00	35.00	18.00

KISKADEE

DRINK POURER, 1970s

This semi-circular pourer, shape 5455/2, has a straight top and base and is decorated with a print of a bird.

Photograph not available
at press time

Backstamp: Unmarked

No.	Description	Colourways	Size	U.S.$	Can.$	U.K.£
1.	Drink Pourer	White; plastic tube; dark green/yellow print; green lettering "Kiskadee"	35 x 40	30.00	35.00	15.00

KOFF FINLAND BEER

ASHTRAY

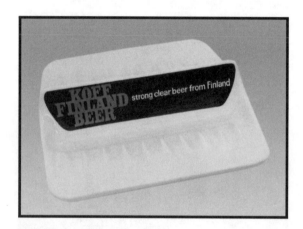

Backstamp: Printed "Wade Regicor London England." laurel leaf frame (large size 18 x 20mm 1953-1962)

No.	Description	Colourways	Size	U.S.$	Can.$	U.K.£
1.	Ashtray	White; black panel; gold/white lettering "Koff Finland Beer strong clear beer from Finland"	Rectangular/190 x 210	12.00	15.00	4.00

KRONENBOURG LAGER

ASHTRAY AND BEER STEINS, 1969-1990

The ashtrays were issued between 1969 and 1990, the beer steins between 1969 and 1984.

Ashtray (No.1)

Beer Stein (No.3)

Beer Stein (No.4)

Backstamp: A. "Wade pdm England"
              B. "Wade P D M England"
              C. Printed "Wade pdm England" (pdm joined 1969-1984)

No.	Description	Colourways	Shape/Size	U.S.$	Can.$	U.K.£
1.	Ashtray	Grey; red/white shield, embossed letters "Kronenbourg"	Castle/90	18.00	22.00	6.00
2.	Ashtray	Grey; gold/red/white lions, shield; white lettering "Kronenbourg"	Square/127	10.00	15.00	5.00
3.	Beer Stein, without cover	Grey; red/white crest, "Kronenbourg"	½ pint/125	20.00	30.00	15.00
4.	Beer Stein, with cover	Grey; red/white crest; pewter lid; gold lettering "Kronenbourg"	Pint/175	60.00	80.00	30.00
5.	Beer Stein, with cover	Grey; red/white crest; pewter lid; gold lettering "Kronenbourg"	1 ½ pint/215	80.00	100.00	40.00

LABATT'S BEER

ASHTRAY AND TANKARDS, 1964-1996

The "Plymouth Tankard" has a gold coloured oval plaque glued on the front which reads "Labatt's Ontario Breweries Department Safety award 1964." The pint barrel tankard has a similar plaque with the inscriptions "Labatts Award" and "Thanks a Million We've brewed and sold a million Barrels this year!" London Plant 1967 under the plaque in black print. The Labatt's traditional tankards were produced in 1967 to the mid-1980s, and the ashtray was produced from 1993-1996.

Million Barrels Tankard (No.2)

Plymouth Tankard (No.3)

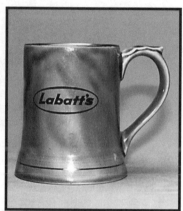
"Labatt's" (No.4)

"Labatt's Blue" (No.5)

"Labatt's 50" (No.6)

Backstamp: A. "Wade P D M Made in England"
           B. "Wade England"

No.	Description	Colourways	Shape/Size	U.S.$	Can.$	U.K.£
1.	Ashtray	Blue; red/white/gold lettering "Labatt's"	Square/210	10.00	15.00	5.00
2.	Million Barrels Tankard	Amber; gold plaque "Labatt's Award;" black lettering "Thanks a Million we've brewed and sold a Million Barrels this year! London Plant 1967"	Pint/125	45.00	70.00	35.00
3.	Plymouth Tankard	Amber; Gold plaque "Labatt's Ontario Breweries Department Safety Award 1964"	Pint/117	45.00	70.00	35.00
4.	Traditional Tankard	Amber; black lettering "Labatt's"	Pint/120	25.00	30.00	12.00
5.	Traditional Tankard	Royal blue; gold lettering "Labatt's Blue"	Pint/120	25.00	30.00	12.00
6.	Traditional Tankard	Royal blue; gold lettering, "Labatt's 50"	Pint/120	25.00	30.00	12.00
7.	Traditional Tankard	White; gold lettering "Labatt's"	Pint/120	25.00	30.00	12.00

LAMB'S NAVY RUM

DRINK POURER

Backstamp: Impressed "5455/1" on underside of button

No.	Description	Colourways	Shape/Size	U.S.$	Can.$	U.K.£
1.	Drink Pourer	White; plastic spout, neck; blue lettering "Lamb's Navy Rum"	Octagonal/40 x 47	15.00	20.00	10.00

RUM JUG

This beautifully decorated decanter was produced in earthenware and is quite heavy. The print is of an 18th century Navy ship *H.M.S. Warrior* surrounded by British Navy flags of the era.

Backstamp: Printed "Genuine Wade Porcelain" (early 1980s)

No.	Description	Colourways	Shape/Size	U.S.$	Can.$	U.K.£
1.	Rum Jug/Decanter	Dark blue/stone; multi-coloured print; white/black lettering	Round/208	85.00	110.00	35.00

LANG BROTHERS LTD

DECANTERS, 1993-1995

These 750 mm decanters were filled with 12-year-old whisky and produced in a limited edition of 4,000. These are the first in a series that celebrates the Chinese New Year. The decanters were available by post direct from Lang Brothers in November 1993 and 1994 at a cost of £95.00 each.

1994 Year of the Dog

1995 Year of the Pig

Backstamp: "Langs ® select 1861 Founders Reserve Scotch Whisky—Genuine Wade Porcelain Gilded with 22 ct. gold"

No.	Description	Colourways	Size	U.S.$	Can.$	U.K.£
1.	1994 Year of the Dog	White; gold/dark blue/pale blue decoration, lettering "Year of the Dog"	235	40.00	75.00	45.00
2.	1995 Year of the Pig	White; gold/dark blue/turquoise/red decoration, lettering "Year of the Pig"	235	40.00	75.00	45.00

WATER JUG

Backstamp: Printed "Wade Regicor London England," a laurel leaf frame (large size 18 x 20 mm 1953-1962)

No.	Description	Colourways	Size	U.S.$	Can.$	U.K.£
1.	Water Jug, open spout	White; black print/lettering "Lang's 'Scotch Whisky Abune them a'"	Rectangular/145	35.00	40.00	18.00

LANGS SUPREME SCOTCH WHISKY

DRINK POURER

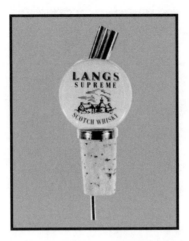

Backstamp: None

No.	Description	Colourways	Shape/Size	U.S.$	Can.$	U.K.£
1.	Drink Pourer	White; metal spout, neck; black/red lettering "Langs Supreme Scotch Whisky"	Round C53/41 x 44	20.00	25.00	12.00

LAPHROAIG SCOTCH WHISKY

DRINK POURER

Backstamp: Impressed "5455/1" on underside of button

No.	Description	Colourways	Size	U.S.$	Can.$	U.K.£
1.	Drink Pourer	White/black; plastic spout, neck; lettering "10 Years Old Laphroaig Unblended Islay Malt Scotch Whisky"	Octagonal/40 x 47	25.00	30.00	10.00

LAUDER'S SCOTCH WHISKY

WATER JUGS, 1969-1984

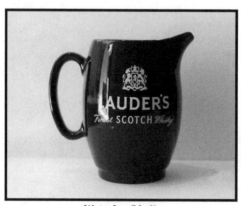

Water Jug (No.1)

Backstamp: A. Printed "Wade pdm" (pdm joined 1969-1984)
B. Printed "Wade pdm England" (pdm separated 1984-1990)

No.	Description	Colourways	Shape/Size	U.S.$	Can.$	U.K.£
1.	Water Jug	Black jug; white crest/lettering "Lauder's Finest Scotch Whisky"	Rectangular/145	30.00	20.00	12.00
2.	Water Jug	Cream jug; black lettering "Lauder's Scotch Whisky"	Round/127	35.00	40.00	20.00

LOMBARD SCOTCH WHISKY

DECANTER, 1993

This decorative decanter has a print of Highland cattle on the shores of a loch, on the label.

Photograph not available
at press time

Backstamp: Printed "Wade England" between two lines and "Made Exclusively for Lombard Scotch Whisky Ltd by Wade England"

No.	Description	Colourways	Shape/Size	U.S.$	Can.$	U.K.£
1.	Decanter	Maroon bottle; gold cap/bands; multi-coloured print; black lettering "Aged 21 Years The Highland gathering"	225	45.00	55.00	25.00

LONG JOHN SCOTCH WHISKY

ASHTRAYS AND WATER JUG, 1955-1984

The ashtrays were produced between 1955 and 1962, the water jug between 1969 and 1984. The jug has an open spout.

Ashtray "Long John Scotch Whisky" (No.1)

Backstamp: **A.** "Wade Regicor, London England," laurel leaves, large size
B. "Wade pdm England"

No.	Description	Colourways	Shape/Size	U.S.$	Can.$	U.K.£
1.	Ashtray	Amber/white; black lettering "Long John Scotch Whisky"	Round/140	15.00	20.00	8.00
2.	Ashtray	Amber/white; black lettering "Long John Scotch Whisky"	Round/153	15.00	20.00	8.00
3.	Water Jug	Black; gold/white lettering "Long John"	Oval/175	25.00	30.00	12.00

LYLE & KINAHAN LTD

WATER JUG, c.1958-1966

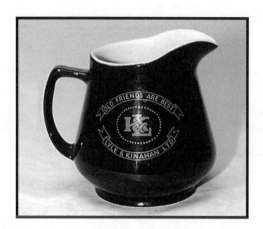

Backstamp: "Porcelain by Wade (Ulster) Ltd Co Armagh N.I."

No.	Description	Colourways	Shape/Size	U.S.$	Can.$	U.K.£
1.	Water Jug, open spout	Black; gold lettering "Old Friends are Best Lyle & Kinahan Ltd"	Round/120	40.00	45.00	20.00

McCALLUM'S SCOTS WHISKY

ASHTRAYS AND DRINK POURERS, c.1960-1984

The triangular ashtray was produced between 1969 and 1984. The circular ashtray has an embossed design of a Scotsman with shield and sword in the centre, with impressed "McCallum's Perfection Scots Whisky" around the sides. The drink pourer, produced circa 1960, is shape number C53, with a straight base.

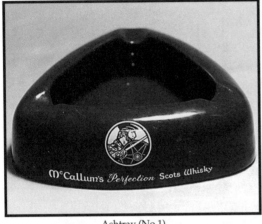

Ashtray (No.1)

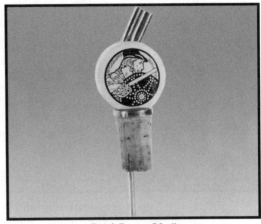

Drink Pourer (No.4)

Backstamp: **A.** "Wade pdm England"
B. "Wade Regicor Made in UK"
C. Printed "Wade Redicor England" (c.1950s)

No.	Description	Colourways	Shape/Size	U.S.$	Can.$	U.K.£
1.	Ashtray	Maroon; white print, lettering "McCallum's Perfection Scots Whisky"	Triangular/159	20.00	30.00	10.00
2.	Ashtray, embossed	Amber; embossed Scotsman; impressed lettering "Mc Callum's Perfection Scots Whisky"	Round/120	65.00	85.00	40.00
3.	Drink Pourer	White; multi-coloured print	Circular/41	30.00	35.00	15.00
4.	Drink Pourer	White; black McCallum print; metal spout, neck; red lettering "McCallum's Whisky"	Oval/C53A/40 x 44	30.00	35.00	15.00

CHARACTER JUGS, c.1950-c.1959

These character jugs are in the form of a bearded Scotsman wearing a glengarry, with the ribbons forming the handle. They were first issued by Wade in the early 1950s, then reissued in collaboration with Regicor in the late 1950s.

 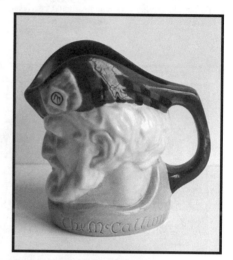

Backstamp: **A.** "Wade Regicor, London, England"
B. "Wade England"
C. "Wade Made in England Hand Painted"

No.	Description	Colourways	Size	U.S.$	Can.$	U.K.£
1.	Character Jug	Amber	Miniature/70	100.00	135.00	65.00
2.	Character Jug	Dark brown/red/black hat; amber face	Miniature/70	125.00	155.00	80.00
3.	Character Jug	Amber	Small/115	85.00	115.00	55.00
4.	Character Jug	Dark brown/red/black hat; amber face	Small/115	95.00	125.00	75.00
5.	Character Jug	Amber	Large/160	75.00	120.00	60.00
6.	Character Jug	Dark brown/red/black hat; amber	Large/160	85.00	110.00	50.00
7.	Character Jug	Dark brown hat; red/black check band; green badge; white hair; pink face, neck; light orange base	Large/160	125.00	160.00	60.00

WATER JUGS, 1969-1984

These jugs have recessed handles and open spouts. Version No. 2 has a print of a Scotsman on it.

Backstamp: "Wade pdm England"

No.	Description	Colourways	Shape/Size	U.S.$	Can.$	U.K.£
1.	Water Jug	Black; white lettering "McCallum's Perfected Scots Whisky"	Round/127	25.00	30.00	12.00
2.	Water Jug	Maroon; white print, lettering "McCallum's Perfected Scots Whisky "	Round/127	25.00	30.00	12.00

MACKENZIE SCOTCH WHISKY

DRINK POURER AND WATER JUG, 1969-1984

The water jug has an open spout. The drink pourer has no backstamp.

Backstamp: "Wade pdm England"

No.	Description	Colourways	Shape/Size	U.S.$	Can.$	U.K.£
1.	Drink Pourer	White; plastic spout, neck; black lettering "The Real MacKenzie Scotch Whisky"	C54/37 x 60 Rectangular	25.00	30.00	15.00
2.	Water Jug	White; black/gold lettering "MacKenzie Whisky"	Square/110	25.00	30.00	12.00

MACKINLAY'S SCOTCH WHISKY

ASHTRAY, 1955-1962

The ashtray was produced between 1955 and 1962.

Photograph not available at press time

Backstamp: Printed "Wade Regicor London England," laurel leaf frame (large size 18 x 20mm 1953-1962)

No.	Description	Colourways	Shape/Size	U.S.$	Can.$	U.K.£
1.	Ashtray	Creamy yellow; red lettering "MacKinlay's Scotch"	Shield/184	30.00	35.00	15.00

DRINK POURERS

Drink Pourer (No.2)

Drink Pourer (No.3)

Drink Pourer (No.5)

Backstamp:
A. "Wade Regicor Made in UK" on the neck
B. Impressed "C52A" under porcelain button not seen unless pourer is taken apart
C. Impressed "5455/1" on underside of button

No.	Description	Colourways	Shape/Size	U.S.$	Can.$	U.K.£
1.	Drink Pourer	White; red/black lettering "MacKinlay's Scotch Whisky"	Round/ C53/41	30.00	35.00	15.00
2.	Drink Pourer	White/yellow; metal spout, tube; brown/black lettering "MacKinlay's Scotch Whisky"	C52A/40 x 48 Octagonal	18.00	25.00	12.00
3.	Drink Pourer	White ; metal spout, tube; black/red lettering "MacKinlay's Old Scotch Whisky"	C52A/40 x 48 Octagonal	18.00	25.00	12.00
4.	Drink Pourer	White/yellow; metal spout, tube; black/red lettering "MacKinlay's Scotch Whisky"	C53/41 x 44 Round	18.00	25.00	12.00
5.	Drink Pourer	White; plastic spout, neck; black/red lettering "MacKinlay's Old Scotch Whisky"	Octagonal/40 x 47	25.00	30.00	10.00

WATER JUG

Photograph not available
at press time

No.	Description	Colourways	Shape/Size	U.S.$	Can.$	U.K.£
1.	Water Jug	Grey; red shield	Cylindrical/163	30.00	20.00	12.00

MACLEAY DUFF SCOTCH WHISKY

ASHTRAY, 1955-1962

Backstamp: "Wade Regicor, London England," laurel leaves, large size

No.	Description	Colourways	Shape/Size	U.S.$	Can.$	U.K.£
1.	Ashtray	Grey; black print; white/black lettering "Macleay Duff Scotch Whisky"	Square/140 clipped corners	15.00	20.00	8.00

MACLEOD'S SCOTCH WHISKY

DECANTER

This beautiful round decanter has an embossed design of the mountains of Skye around the base, and the transfer printed label in an oval recess on the front of the decanter has a picture of the Isle of Skye.

Backstamp: Printed "Wade pdm England" (pdm separated 1984-1990)

No.	Description	Colourways	Shape/Size	U.S.$	Can.$	U.K.£
1.	Decanter	White cap/neck; pale blue/blue bottle; gold/blue label; gold lettering "Macleod's Isle of Skye Blended Scotch Whisky 21 Years Old"	Round/147	45.00	60.00	30.00

WATER JUG, 1984-1990

This water jug has an ice-check spout.

Backstamp: "Wade p d m England"

No.	Description	Colourways	Shape/Size	U.S.$	Can.$	U.K.£
1.	Water Jug	Yellow; brown lettering "Macleod's Isle of Skye 8 yr old Blend"	Rectangular/133	25.00	30.00	12.00

McEWAN'S LAGER

WATER JUG

Backstamp: Printed "Wade pdm England" (pdm separated 1984-1990)

No.	Description	Colourways	Shape/Size	U.S.$	Can.$	U.K.£
1.	Water Jug	Dark blue; blue panel/print; yellow lettering "McEwan's Lager"	Rectangular/190	30.00	35.00	12.00

McMULLEN'S ALES

ASHTRAYS, 1955-1968

Photograph not available
at press time

Backstamp: A. "Wade Regicor, London England," laurel leaves, large size
B. "Wade Regicor, London England," laurel leaves, small size

No.	Description	Colourways	Shape/Size	U.S.$	Can.$	U.K.£
1.	Ashtray	White; red horse, wagon, lettering "McMullen's Ales"	Round/133	15.00	20.00	8.00
2.	Ashtray	White; red lettering "McMullen's Ales"	Round/140	15.00	20.00	8.00

MANSFIELD ALES

ASHTRAYS, 1955-1984

Backstamp: A. "Wade Regicor, London England," laurel leaves, large size
B. "Wade pdm England"

No.	Description	Colourways	Shape/Size	U.S.$	Can.$	U.K.£
1.	Ashtray	Pale green; black/green lettering "Mansfield Ales"	Round/140	15.00	20.00	8.00
2.	Ashtray	Green; yellow logo, lettering "Mansfield Ales"	Square/205	10.00	15.00	5.00

MARKSMAN

ASHTRAY, 1984-1990

The print on this ashtray is of a hand holding an empty glass.

Backstamp: "Wade P D M England"

No.	Description	Colourways	Shape/Size	U.S.$	Can.$	U.K.£
1.	Ashtray	Blue/pink; white/yellow print white lettering "Down with Marksman"	Round/216	10.00	15.00	5.00

MARSTON'S

ASHTRAY, 1991-1996

Photograph not available
at press time

Backstamp: "Wade P D M Made in England"

No.	Description	Colourways	Size	U.S.$	Can.$	U.K.£
1.	Oval	Dark blue; gold lettering "Marston's Head Brewers Choice"	171	15.00	20.00	8.00

MARTELL

DRINK POURERS, c.1970

The No. 1 and 2 pourers are shape C53, which has a straight base. The No. 3 pourer is shape 5455/1. No. 4, which is shape number C52A, has a notched base and shoulders.

Backstamp: Unmarked

No.	Description	Colourways	Shape/Size	U.S.$	Can.$	U.K.£
1.	Drink Pourer	White; red/black lettering "Martell Brandy"	Circular/40	30.00	35.00	15.00
2.	Drink Pourer	White; blue lettering "Martell Brandy"	Circular/41	30.00	35.00	15.00
3.	Drink Pourer	Cream; plastic tube; black/gold lettering "Martell Cognac"	Octagonal/40	30.00	35.00	15.00
4.	Drink Pourer	Cream; plastic tube; black/gold lettering "Martell Cognac"	Square/38	30.00	35.00	15.00

MARTINI

ASHTRAY, 1968-1969

Backstamp: "Reginald Corfield Limited Redhill Surrey," "Wade Regicor England"

No.	Description	Colourways	Shape/Size	U.S.$	Can.$	U.K.£
1.	Ashtray	White; red/black; white lettering "Martini"	Round/210	15.00	20.00	8.00

M. C. COYLE & SONS
DUNDEE WINE SELLERS

DRINK POURER

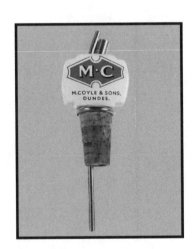

Backstamp: Impressed "C52A" under porcelain button, not seen unless pourer is taken apart

No.	Description	Colourways	Shape/Size	U.S.$	Can.$	U.K.£
1.	Drink Pourer	White/red; metal spout, neck; white/black lettering "M C M. Coyle & Sons, Dundee"	C52A/40 x 48	30.00	35.00	12.00

MITCHELL & BUTLER BEER

WATER JUG, 1979

A special-edition water jug was produced for Mitchell & Butler to mark its centenary. It is in the shape of a Dutch jug, which is round and squat with an open spout. The jug bears the dates 1879-1979 and is highly decorated with ears of barley and bunches of hops.

Photograph not available
at press time

Backstamp: Black transfer print "This Jug has been produced in a limited edition to mark the 100 yrs that have passed since beer was first brewed at the Cope Hill Brewery of Mitchell and Butler. Supplied by Wade PDM Ltd"

No.	Description	Colourways	Shape/Size	U.S.$	Can.$	U.K.£
1.	Water Jug	White; blue/green/honey brown decoration, lettering "M & B Centenary Jug"	Round/140	120.00	150.00	60.00

MORLAND BEER

ASHTRAY AND DRINK POURER, c.1970, 1984-1990

The ashtray was produced between 1984 and 1990 and bears a print of a man with a beer barrel. The pourer, which is shape number 5455/1, was produced circa 1970.

Photograph not available
at press time

Backstamp: A. "Wade P D M England"
B. Unmarked

No.	Description	Colourways	Shape/Size	U.S.$	Can.$	U.K.£
1.	Ashtray	Black; red/white print; white lettering "Morland Brewers since 1711"	Square/140	10.00	15.00	5.00
2.	Pourer	Black; plastic tube; white lettering "Morland Brewers since 1711"	Octagonal/40	30.00	35.00	15.00

MOUNT GAY BARBADOS RUM

ASHTRAY, 1969-1984

The print on this ashtray is of a map of Barbados.

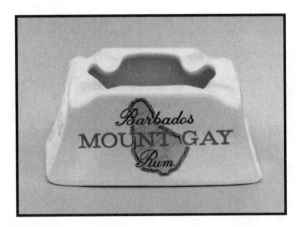

Backstamp: **A.** "Wade pdm England"
B. Printed circular "Reginald Corfield Limited, Redhill Surrey" with "Regicor Wade England" through the circle (1968-1969)

No.	Description	Colourways	Shape/Size	U.S.$	Can.$	U.K.£
1.	Ashtray	White; yellow print; red/black lettering "Mount Gay Barbados Rum"	Square/133	10.00	15.00	5.00
2.	Ashtray	Cream; yellow map of Barbados; black/red lettering "Barbados Mount Gay Rum"	133	12.00	18.00	6.00

NICHOLSON'S GIN

ASHTRAY AND WATER JUGS, 1955-1969

The ashtray was produced between 1955 and 1962 and bears a print of a lamp lighter. The jug, which has an ice-check spout, was produced between 1968 and 1969.

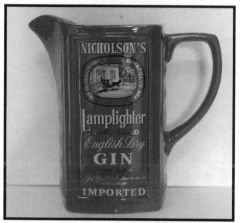

Water Jug (No.2)

Water Jug (No.3)

Ashtray

Backstamp: A. "Wade Regicor, London England," laurel leaves, large size
B. "Reginald Corfield Limited Redhill Surrey," "Wade Regicor England"

No.	Description	Colourways	Shape/Size	U.S.$	Can.$	U.K.£
1.	Ashtray	White; black print; black/red lettering "Nicholson's Lamplighter Gin"	Round/133	20.00	30.00	10.00
2.	Water Jug, ice-check spout	Dark grey; red/white lettering "Nicholson's Lamplighter English Dry Gin"	Rectangular/153	35.00	45.00	22.00
3.	Water Jug, open spout	White; black print; black/red lettering "Nicholson's Lamplighter Distilled London Dry Gin"	Round/153	35.00	45.00	22.00

OLD CHARTER BOURBON

WATER JUG, 1968-1969

Backstamp: A. "Reginald Corfield Limited Redhill Surrey," "Wade Regicor England- 86 proof Kentucky Straight Bourbon Whisky - Old Charter Distillery Co. Louisville, K.Y."

No.	Description	Colourways	Shape/Size	U.S.$	Can.$	U.K.£
1.	Water Jug/ open spout	White; multi-coloured design; red/black lettering "Old Charter Aged Kentucky Bourbon"	Round/165	35.00	45.00	22.00

OLD COURT SCOTCH WHISKY
A. GILLIES & CO (DISTILLERIES) LTD

WATER JUG

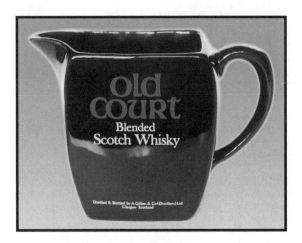

Backstamp: Green printed "Wade pdm" (pdm joined 1969-1984)

No.	Description	Colourways	Shape/Size	U.S.$	Can.$	U.K.£
1.	Water Jug	Black; red/white lettering "Old Court Blended Scotch Whisky Distilled & Bottled by A. Gillies & Co (Distilleries) Ltd Glasgow Scotland"	Square/125	30.00	35.00	12.00

OLD PARR SCOTCH WHISKY
MACDONALD GREENLEES LTD.

ASHTRAY, DECANTERS, DRINK POURER AND WATER JUG, 1969-1984

Decanter, pewter stopper

Decanter, porcelain stopper

Ashtray

Drink Pourer

Backstamp: **A.** "Wade pdm England"
B. Printed "Royal Victoria Pottery, Staffordshire England MacDonald Greenlees Ltd. Distillers, Edinburgh, Scotland"
C. Impressed "5455/1" on underside of button

No.	Description	Colourways	Shape/Size	U.S.$	Can.$	U.K.£
1.	Ashtray	Maroon; white lettering "Old Parr Real Antique & Rare Old Scotch Whisky"	Round/153	15.00	20.00	8.00
2.	Decanter, pewter stopper	Blue; gold labels; black/gold lettering "Old Parr 500 Fifteen Year Old Blended Scotch Whisky"	Round/225	18.00	25.00	10.00
3.	Decanter, porcelain stopper	Black; gold labels; black/gold lettering "Old Parr 500 Fifteen Year Old Blended Scotch Whisky"	Round/225	18.00	25.00	10.00
4.	Drink Pourer	White; plastic spout, neck; red lettering "Grand Old Parr"	Octagonal/40 x 47	25.00	30.00	12.00
5.	Water Jug	Maroon; white lettering "Old Parr Real Antique & Rare Old Scotch Whisky"	Round/133	30.00	35.00	15.00

OLD RARITY SCOTCH WHISKY

DRINK POURER AND WATER JUG

The jug, produced between 1984-1990, has an open spout.

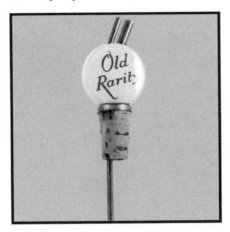

Backstamp: "Wade p d m England"

No.	Description	Colourways	Shape/Size	U.S.$	Can.$	U.K.£
1.	Drink Pourer	White; metal spout, neck; red lettering; (Front)"Old Rarity" (Back) "Bulloch Lade 'B L' Scotch Whisky"	Round C53/41 x 44	25.00	30.00	12.00
2.	Water Jug	White; red lettering "Old Rarity De Luxe Scotch Whisky"	Square/127	25.00	30.00	12.00

OLD SMUGGLER SCOTCH WHISKY

WATER JUG

Backstamp: Green printed "Wade pdm" (pdm joined 1969-1984)

No.	Description	Colourways	Shape/Size	U.S.$	Can.$	U.K.£
1.	Water Jug, ice-check spout	Black; white lettering "Old Smuggler Scotch Whisky"	Rectangular/165	35.00	40.00	15.00

ORANJEBOOM LAGER

ASHTRAYS, 1969-1990

The print on these ashtrays is of a tree.

Photograph not available
at press time

Backstamp: **A.** "Wade pdm England"
B. "Wade p d m England"

No.	Description	Colourways	Shape/Size	U.S.$	Can.$	U.K.£
1.	Ashtray	Black; orange print; white lettering "Oranjeboom Lager Beer"	Oval/210	15.00	20.00	8.00
2.	Ashtray	Black; red print; white/green lettering "Oranjeboom"	Oval/210	10.00	15.00	5.00

O.V.D. RUM

DRINK POURER

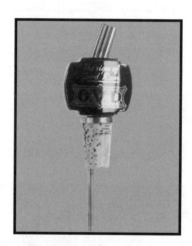

Backstamp: Impressed "5455/1" on underside of button

No.	Description	Colourways	Size	U.S.$	Can.$	U.K.£
1.	Drink Pourer	Black; metal spout, neck; gold lettering "The Sign of Good Rum O.V.D."	C52A/40 x 48 Octagonal	30.00	35.00	12.00

PADDY IRISH WHISKEY

DRINK POURER AND WATER JUG, 1969-1984

This pourer has a notched base and shoulders, with a metal tube. It is shape number C52A.

Backstamp: A. "Wade pdm England"
              B. Unmarked

No.	Description	Colourways	Shape/Size	U.S.$	Can.$	U.K.£
1.	Drink Pourer	White; yellow/black lettering "Paddy Old Irish Whiskey"	Square/38	30.00	35.00	15.00
2.	Water Jug, ice-check spout	Brown; multi-coloured lettering "Paddy Old Irish Whiskey"	Round/165	30.00	35.00	15.00

216

PARKERS SCOTCH WHISKY

DECANTER

Backstamp: Unknown

No.	Description	Colourways	Shape/Size	U.S.$	Can.$	U.K.£
1.	Decanter	Black; multi-coloured Piper and Hounds print, gold lettering "Parkers Finest Scotch Whisky 70cle 40% vol"	Round/230	40.00	55.00	20.00

PASSPORT SCOTCH WHISKY

ASHTRAY

Backstamp: Transfer print "Wade pdm England" (pdm joined 1969-1984)

No.	Description	Colourways	Shape/Size	U.S.$	Can.$	U.K.£
1.	Ashtray	Olive green; multi-coloured print; white lettering "Passport Scotch Whisky"	Square/125	12.00	18.00	8.00

PERNOD

ASHTRAYS AND DRINK POURERS, 1995-1996

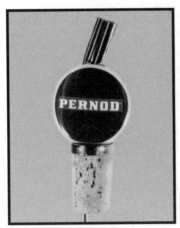

Drink Pourer (No.3)   Drink Pourer (No.4)

Backstamp: "Wade P D M Made in England"

No.	Description	Colourways	Shape/Size	U.S.$	Can.$	U.K.£
1.	Ashtray	Dark blue; red/white lettering "Pernod Cafe des pres"	Square/159	10.00	15.00	5.00
2.	Ashtray	Dark blue; red/white lettering "Pernod Cafe des pres"	Square/184	10.00	15.00	5.00
3.	Drink Pourer	White/black; metal spout, tube; red bar; white lettering "Pernod"	Round C53/41 x 44	25.00	30.00	12.00
4.	Drink Pourer	White/blue; metal spout, tube; red bar; white lettering "Pernod"	Round C53/41 x 44	25.00	30.00	12.00

PETER DAWSON SCOTCH WHISKY

DRINK POURER

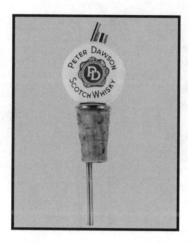

No.	Description	Colourways	Size	U.S.$	Can.$	U.K.£
1.	Drink Pourer	White; metal spout, neck; blue lettering "Peter Dawson PD Scotch Whisky"	C53/41 x 44 Round	25.00	30.00	12.00

PETER THOMPSON (PERTH) LTD.

CHESS SET, 1979-c.1982, The Thistle And The Rose

The matt biscuit-porcelain chess set was produced (by Wade Ireland) exclusively for Peter Thompson Ltd. The models were designed by Ann Whittet and modelled by Frederick Mellor (indicated on the backstamps by WFM). The master pieces represent the royal house of Scotland (the thistle) and the royal house of England (the rose). The pawns resemble a ship's decanter and have no backstamps. They were originally issued as a boxed set, complete with a copper and brass chess board, which pulled out from the bottom of the box like a drawer. Included in the box was a bottle of Beneagles Scotch Whisky; the chess pieces were unfilled. The principal pieces could be purchased individually as whisky miniatures filled with 1 2/3 ounces (50 millilitres) of Beneagles Scotch Whisky. The pawns were too small to fill, so were not issued individually. At the end of 1980, the remainder of the chess pieces were exported to North America. A large number went to the to the Las Vegas Distributing Company and also to the Jon-Sol Company of Milwaukee, Wisconsin. They were sold as a boxed pair, a chessman and a pawn in a gold-and-black chequered box; only the master pieces were filled with whisky. The boxed pair was also sold in Ontario, Canada, for $5.00 a pair, with a Liquor Control Board of Ontario label. In the early 1980s the black chess pieces were produced in a gloss glaze. They were given as complimentary gifts to first-class passengers on British Caledonian Airways or could be purchased from the airlines by mail order.

The Rose Chess Pieces

The Thistle Chess Pieces

Backstamp: Embossed "Beneagles Scotch Whisky"

The Rose Chess Pieces, White

No.	Name	Finish	Size	U.S.$	Can.$	U.K.£
1.	King Henry VIII	Matt	134	28.00	38.00	15.00
2.	Queen Elizabeth I	Matt	133	28.00	38.00	15.00
3.	Bishop Thomas à Becket	Matt	135	28.00	38.00	15.00
4.	Knight—Sir Francis Drake	Matt	130	28.00	38.00	15.00
5.	Castle—Norman English Tower	Matt	100	28.00	38.00	15.00
6.	Pawn	Matt	95	32.00	45.00	18.00

The Thistle Chess Pieces, Black

No.	Name	Finish	Size	U.S.$	Can.$	U.K.£
7.	Mary, Queen of Scots	Matt	125	28.00	38.00	15.00
8.	Mary, Queen of Scots	Gloss	125	28.00	38.00	15.00
9.	King Robert the Bruce	Matt	130	28.00	38.00	15.00
10.	King Robert the Bruce	Gloss	130	28.00	38.00	15.00
11.	Bishop John Knox	Matt	128	28.00	38.00	15.00
12.	Bishop John Knox	Gloss	128	28.00	38.00	15.00
13.	Knight — Sir William Wallace	Matt	135	28.00	38.00	15.00
14.	Knight — Sir William Wallace	Gloss	135	28.00	38.00	15.00
15.	Castle — Scottish Tower House	Matt	102	28.00	38.00	15.00
16.	Castle — Scottish Tower House	Gloss	102	28.00	38.00	15.00
17.	Pawn	Matt	100	32.00	45.00	18.00
18.	Pawn	Gloss	100	32.00	45.00	18.00

CURLING-STONE CONTAINERS, 1975-1981

These circular curling stone containers were first produced for Peter Thompson in 1975 for Air Canada's duty free shops. Printed on top of version No. 1 is "World Curling Championship, Air Canada Silver Broom, Perth Scotland 1975."

Curling Stone (No.1)

Curling Stone (No.2)

Backstamp: **A:** Embossed "Beneagles Scotch Whisky, Wade 74"
B: Embossed "Beneagles Scotch Whisky, Wade Ireland"

No.	Name	Colourways	Size	U.S.$	Can.$	U.K.£
1.	Air Canada Curling Stone	Light grey/dark grey flecks; black handle; tartan ribbon; black lettering "Wolrd Curling Championshop, Air Canada Silver Broom, Perth Scotland 1975"	65	70.00	90.00	35.00
2.	Curling Stone	Light grey/dark grey flecks; black handle; tartan ribbon	65	50.00	70.00	25.00

WHISKY MINIATURES, 1981 - c.1985

Golf Ball whisky miniature (No. 2)

Grizzly Bar whisky miniature (No. 3)

Backstamp: **A.** "Beneagles Scotch Whisky - Peter Thompson, (Perth) Ltd Scotland"
B. Unmarked

No.	Name	Colourways	Size	U.S.$	Can.$	U.K.£
1.	Golden Eagle	Dark brown; grey/brown rock	110	70.00	90.00	35.00
2.	Golf Ball	White; red lettering "3 Peter Thomson's"	Round/50	10.00	15.00	5.00
3.	Grizzly Bear	Dark brown	120	98.00	130.00	65.00

PIMM'S
UNITED DISTILLERS UK PLC

DRINK POURERS

This pourer, shape number C62, was produced with either a plastic or metal tube.

Drink Pourer (No.2)   Drink Pourer (No.3)

Backstamp: A: Unmarked
B: Impressed "5455/1" on underside of button

No.	Description	Colourways	Shape/Size	U.S.$	Can.$	U.K.£
1.	Drink Pourer	White; red/black/gold lettering "Pimm's"	Rectangular/48	30.00	35.00	15.00
2.	Drink Pourer	White; metal spout, neck; black crown; red/black lettering "Pimm's Pimm's Limited London"	C62/47 x 41 Rectangular	25.00	30.00	15.00
3.	Drink Pourer	White; plastic spout, neck; red lettering "Pimm's"	Octagonal/40 x 47	25.00	30.00	10.00

PIPER SCOTCH WHISKY

ASHTRAYS, 1962-1968

Backstamp: **A:** "Wade Regicor, London England," laurel leaves, large size
B: Printed "Wade - Regicor London England," laurel leaf frame (small size 13 x 13mm 1962-late 1968)

No.	Description	Colourways	Shape/Size	U.S.$	Can.$	U.K.£
1.	Ashtray	White; black print; black/red lettering "Piper Extra Export Ale"	Square/140	20.00	28.00	8.00
2.	Ashtray	Yellow; black print; black/red lettering "Piper Scotch Whisky"	145 mm	20.00	28.00	8.00

BAR LAMP

Backstamp: Printed "Wade Regicor Made in Great Britain" in laurel leaf frame

No.	Description	Colourways	Shape/Size	U.S.$	Can.$	U.K.£
1.	Bar Lamp	White base; red/black print in frame; shade red; red/black print in frame; cream lettering "Piper Export The Most Satisfying Export"	Base Cube/115	70.00	85.00	45.00

PLYMOUTH GIN

WATER JUG, 1968-1969

This water jug has an ice-check spout and is decorated with a print of the bottle label.

Photograph not available
at press time

Backstamp: "Reginald Corfield Limited Redhill Surrey," "Wade Regicor England"

No.	Description	Colourways	Shape/Size	U.S.$	Can.$	U.K.£
1.	Water Jug	White; red/blue print, lettering "Plymouth Dry Gin Distilled in England Since 1783"	Square/153	30.00	35.00	15.00

PRESIDENT SPECIAL

ASHTRAY, 1969-1984

This ashtray is decorated with a print of a shield.

Photograph not available
at press time

Backstamp: "Wade pdm England"

No.	Description	Colourways	Shape/Size	U.S.$	Can.$	U.K.£
1.	Ashtray	Cream; gold print; black/white lettering "President Special Reserve"	Rectangular/177	10.00	15.00	5.00

PUSSER'S RUM

DECANTERS, 1983-1996

Ship's decanters are heavy and very wide at the bottom, giving them stability in rough seas. All Pusser's Rum decanters are sealed with red wax, and ceramic-capped corks are attached by a cord to the handles.

Admiral Lord Nelson, 1983-1996

One-Litre Decanter (front)   One-Litre Decanter (back)

Backstamp: "Nelson Finest English Porcelain Wade Staffordshire England"

No.	Description	Colourways	Size	U.S.$	Can.$	U.K.£
1.	Decanter	White: blue cap/neck; multi-coloured prints	Miniature/90	40.00	45.00	20.00
2.	Decanter	Blue/white; multi-coloured prints	One Litre/240	95.00	135.00	50.00

John Paul Jones, 1994-1995

Backstamp: "Pusser's Ltd. British Virgin Islands, West Indies, The John Paul Jones - U.S. Navy and Marine Corps Decanter"

No.	Description	Colourways	Size	U.S.$	Can.$	U.K.£
1.	Decanter	Blue/white; multi-coloured prints	220	60.00	80.00	30.00

HIP FLASKS, 1981-1996

Royal Navy Rum Terminology (front)

Royal Navy Rum Terminology (back)

Backstamp: **A:** Embossed "Made in England"
B: Embossed "Hand Cast Porcelain Made in England"

No.	Name	Colourways	Size	U.S.$	Can.$	U.K.£
1.	Toasts	Blue/white; multi-coloured label	146	60.00	80.00	30.00
2.	West Indies	Blue/white; multi-coloured label	150	60.00	80.00	30.00
3.	Terminology	Blue/white; multi-coloured prints	146	70.00	90.00	35.00
4.	America's Cup Challenge	Blue/white; multi-coloured print	146	70.00	90.00	35.00

RUM JUGS

Jolly Jack, 1981

Jolly Jack Pusser's Rum Jug (front)

Jolly Jack Pusser's Rum Jug (back)

Backstamp: "Wade Made in England"

No.	Name	Colourways	Size	U.S.$	Can.$	U.K.£
1.	Jolly Jack Pusser's Rum Jug	Blue/white; blue cap; multi-coloured prints	200	55.00	65.00	30.00

Miniature Rum Jug, 1981

Miniature Jug (front)

Miniature Jug (back)

Backstamp: Unmarked

No.	Description	Colourways	Size	U.S.$	Can.$	U.K.£
1.	Miniature Rum Jug	Blue/white; blue cap	63	35.00	45.00	20.00

Nelson's Rum Jug, 1981

The front of this colourful jug has the words "Nelson's Blood" with the Pusser's label on the front, and on the back is a map of Drake's voyage. Pusser's Rum has been part of the Royal Navy tradition for centuries, with the Royal Navy Sailors Fund receiving a substantial donation from its worldwide sales.

Nelson's Blood (front)

Nelson's Blood (back)

Backstamp: Printed "British Navy Pusser's Rum Botled by Pusser's Ltd, British Virgin Islands
Product of the British Virgin Islands 750 ml. 95.5 Proof 47.75 ALC/Vol"

No.	Name	Colourways	Size	U.S.$	Can.$	U.K.£
1.	Nelson's Rum Jug	Blue/white; blue cap; multi-coloured prints "Nelson's Blood "	200	50.00	58.00	25.00

WATER JUG, 1996

This water jug has a recessed handle and open spout. It has a print of the Pusser's Rum label on the front and the traditional toasts of the Royal Navy on the back.

Water Jug (front)

Water Jug (back)

Backstamp: "Royal Victoria Pottery Staffordshire England"

No.	Description	Colourways	Shape/Size	U.S.$	Can.$	U.K.£
1.	Water Jug	White; blue rim; multi-coloured prints	Round/146	30.00	35.00	12.00

QUEEN ANNE SCOTCH WHISKY
HILL THOMSON CO. LTD.

ASHTRAYS, 1955-1962

The ashtrays were produced between 1955 and 1962, the water jugs between 1955 and 1990.

Ashtray (No.2)

Ashtray (No.4)

Backstamp: A: "Wade Regicor, London England," laurel leaves, large size (1953-1962)
B: "Wade p d m England"

No.	Description	Colourways	Shape/Size	U.S.$	Can.$	U.K.£
1.	Ashtray	Black; grey/gold crest; white lettering "Queen Anne Rare Scotch Whisky"	Round/153	15.00	20.00	8.00
2.	Ashtray	Black; white lettering "Queen Anne Rare Scotch Whisky"	Square/146 clipped corners	15.00	20.00	8.00
3.	Ashtray	Black; grey/gold crest; white lettering "Queen Anne Rare Scotch Whisky"	Square/153	15.00	20.00	8.00
4.	Ashtray	Black; green lettering & coat of arms "Queen Anne Scotch Whisky By Appointment to Her Majesty The Queen Suppliers of Scotch Whisky Hill Thomson -Co LTD"	Round/120	10.00	12.00	6.00

DRINK POURERS

Drink Pourer (No.1)

Drink Pourer (No.2)

Drink Pourer (No.3)

Backstamp **A:** Impressed "5455/1" on underside of button.
B: Printed "Wade Regicor England"

No	Description	Colourways	Shape/Size	U.S.$	Can.$	U.K.£
1.	Drink Pourer	White/black; plastic spout, neck; white lettering "Queen Anne Rare Scotch Whisky"	5455/140 x 47 Octagonal	25.00	30.00	10.00
2.	Drink Pourer	White / black; metal spout, neck; white lettering "Scotch Queen Anne Whisky"	C53/41 x 44 Round	30.00	35.00	12.00
3.	Drink Pourer	Black all porcelain; white lettering "Queen Anne"	97	35.00	40.00	18.00

WATER JUGS, 1955-1990

Water Jug (No.2)

Water Jug (No.3)

No.	Description	Colourways	Shape/Size	U.S.$	Can.$	U.K.£
1.	Water Jug, ice-check spout	Mottled stone; black lettering "Queen Anne Scotch Whisky"	Round/177	25.00	30.00	12.00
2.	Water Jug, open spout	Black; multi-coloured print, white lettering "Queen Anne Scotch Whisky"	Round/127	25.00	30.00	12.00
3.	Water Jug	Black; white lettering "Queen Anne Rare Scotch Whisky"	Round/127	25.00	30.00	10.00

RAWLINGS MIXERS

DRINK POURERS, c.1970, c.1980

These pourers are shape number 5455/1 and came with plastic tubes. Some of them bear no backstamp.

Drink Pourer (No.3)

Drink Pourer (No.4)

Drink Pourer (No.5)

Drink Pourer (No.6)

Backstamp: Impressed "5455/1" on underside of button

No.	Description	Colourways	Shape/Size	U.S.$	Can.$	U.K.£
1.	Drink Pourer	Yellow/black; gold lettering "Rawlings"	Octagonal/40	30.00	35.00	15.00
2.	Drink Pourer	White/yellow; black lettering "Rawlings Mixing Waters"	Octagonal/40	30.00	35.00	15.00
3.	Drink Pourer	White/black; plastic spout, neck; black lettering "Rawlings"	C54/37 x 60 Rectangular	25.00	30.00	15.00
4.	Drink Pourer	Yellow/black band; plastic spout and neck; red/black lettering "Rawlings Established 1784 Mixing Waters"	5455/140 x 47 Octagonal	25.00	30.00	10.00
5.	Drink Pourer	Yellow/brown band; plastic spout, neck black/brown lower case lettering "Rawlings Established 1784"	5455/140 x 47 Octagonal	25.00	30.00	10.00
6.	Drink Pourer	Yellow/brown band; plastic spout, neck black/brown lettering "Rawlings Established 1784 Mixing Waters"	5455/140 x 47 Octagonal	25.00	30.00	10.00

REBEL YELL

DRINK POURER, 1995

This pourer has a rounded top and base and straight sides; it is shape number C57. It was produced with a metal tube.

Backstamp: Unmarked

No.	Description	Colourways	Size	U.S.$	Can.$	U.K.£
1.	Drink Pourer	White; grey lettering "Rebel Yell"	41	30.00	35.00	15.00

THE REVEREND JAMES ALE

TANKARD

This bulbous pint tankard is rimmed in gold lustre and decorated with a portrait of the Reverend James. It has a large round handle.

Photograph not available
at press time

No.	Description	Colourways	Size	U.S.$	Can.$	U.K.£
1.	Tankard	White; gold rim; black/red print	112	25.00	30.00	12.00

ROBYN HOODE DISTILLERIES

DECANTERS, 1993

The decanters are shaped as medieval hunting horns. The black and gold cords can be found on either colour decanter.

Backstamp: "Wade - England"

No.	Description	Colourways	Size	U.S.$	Can.$	U.K.£
1.	Decanter	Black decanter, stand, cord; gold decoration , lettering "Spirit of Robyn Hoode Aged malt Whisky Specially Selected for Robyn Hoode Distilleries, Elston, newark, Nottinghamshire Wade England"	360	100.00	135.00	65.00
2.	Decanter	White decanter, stand, cord; gold decoration, lettering "Spirit of Robyn Hoode Aged malt Whisky Specially Selected for Robyn Hoode Distilleries, Elston, newark, Nottinghamshire Wade England"	360	100.00	135.00	65.00

ROMANOFF VODKA

ASHTRAY AND WATER JUGS, 1969-1990

The ashtray was issued between 1984 and 1990. Jug No. 2, which has an open spout and is decorated with a print of two eagles, was issued between 1969 and 1984. Jug No. 3 has a recessed handle and open spout.

Water Jug (No.3)

Backstamp: **A:** "Wade pdm England"
B: "Wade p d m England"

No.	Description	Colourways	Shape/Size	U.S.$	Can.$	U.K.£
1.	Ashtray	Black; white/red lettering "Romanoff Vodka"	Square/140	10.00	15.00	5.00
2.	Water Jug, open spout	Black; gold print; red/white/black lettering "Romanoff Vodka"	Round/205	30.00	40.00	20.00
3.	Water Jug, open spout	Black/dark red; gold crest; White lettering "Romanoff Vodka Prince of all the Vodkas;" black signature	Round/200	30.00	40.00	20.00

RUDDLES COUNTY

ASHTRAY

Backstamp: Printed "Wade pdm England" (pdm separated 1984-1990)

No.	Description	Colourways	Shape/size	U.S.$	Can.$	U.K.£
1.	Ashtray	Black; white print, lettering "Ruddles County"	Square/138	10.00	12.00	6.00

SACCONE & SPEED

ASHTRAYS, 1962-1968

Backstamp: A: "Wade Regicor, London England," laurel leaves, large size
B: "Wade Regicor, London England," laurel leaves, small size

No.	Description	Colourways	Shape/Size	U.S.$	Can.$	U.K.£
1.	Ashtray	Black; white lettering "Saccone & Speed"	Round/140	15.00	20.00	8.00
2.	Ashtray	Black; white print lettering "Ruddles County"	Square/138	10.00	12.00	6.00
3.	Ashtray	Black; white print lettering "Ruddles County"	Square/138	10.00	12.00	6.00

SAINT BRENDAN'S SUPERIOR

DRINK POURER

Backstamp: None

No.	Description	Colourways	Shape/Size	U.S.$	Can.$	U.K.£
1.	Drink Pourer	Cream; metal spout & neck; gold lower case lettering "Saint Brendan's Superior"	C53/41 x 44 Round	30.00	35.00	12.00

SALIGNAC COGNAC

DRINK POURER

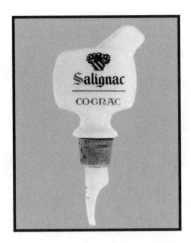

Backstamp: None

No.	Description	Colourways	Shape/size	U.S.$	Can.$	U.K.£
1.	Drink Pourer	White; all porcelain; red, black lettering "Salignac Cognac"	Rectangular AP5/117	30.00	35.00	15.00

SAMUEL WEBSTER

ASH BOWL, 1984-1990

Backstamp: "Wade p d m England"

No.	Description	Colourways	Shape/Size	U.S.$	Can.$	U.K.£
1.	Ash Bowl	Green; cream print, lettering "Samuel Webster 1838 Halifax Yorkshire"	Circular/250	30.00	35.00	15.00

SCOTS GREY BLENDED SCOTCH WHISKY

WATER JUG

This unusual shaped jug has an ice-check spout and slanted shoulders.

Backstamp: Printed "Wade pdm England" (pdm joined 1969-1984)

No.	Description	Colourways	Shape/Size	U.S.$	Can.$	U.K.£
1.	Water Jug, ice-check spout	Black; white print; white, gold lettering "Scots Grey Blended Scotch Whisky"	Rectangular/165	35.00	40.00	18.00

SEAGRAM'S SCOTCH WHISKY

DRINK POURER AND WATER JUGS, 1984-1990

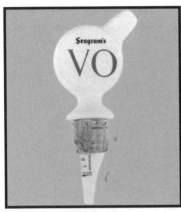

Drink Pourer

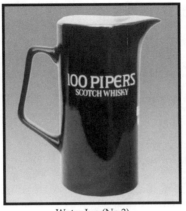

Water Jug (No.3)

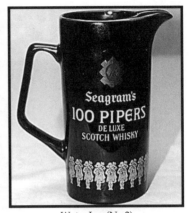

Water Jug (No.2)

Backstamp A: "Wade p d m England"
B: Printed "Wade Regicor Made in England," laurel leaf frame

No.	Description	Colourways	Shape/Size	U.S.$	Can.$	U.K.£
1.	Drink Pourer	White; all porcelain; black/red lettering "Seagram's VO"	AP2/117	25.00	30.00	15.00
2.	Water Jug, ice-check spout	Black; gold print; white lettering "Seagram's 100 Pipers De Luxe Scotch Whisky"	Round/175	25.00	30.00	12.00
3.	Water Jug, ice-check spout	Black; white lettering "100 Pipers Scotch Whisky"	Round/175	35.00	40.00	18.00

SEVEN SEAS RUM

DRINK POURER

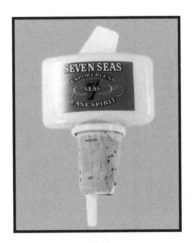

No.	Description	Colourways	Shape/Size	U.S.$	Can.$	U.K.£
1.	Drink Pourer	White / blue; plastic spout, neck; white lettering "Seven Seas Export Blend 7 Seas Can Spirit"	C54/37 x 60 Rectangular	25.00	30.00	15.00

SHEPHERD NEAME

ASHTRAYS

Ashtray (No.1)

Ashtray (No.2)

Backstamp : Printed circular "Wade P D M" (p d m separated 1984-1990)

No.	Description	Colourways	Shape/Size	U.S.$	Can.$	U.K.£
1.	Ashtray	Cream; red/yellow print; white/yellow lettering "Hurlimann Stern Brau Hurlimann Swiss Lager Brewed in U.K. By Shepherd Neame"	Square/173	12.00	15.00	8.00
2.	Ashtray	Cream; brown/orange print; white/orange lettering "Master Brew Bitter Shepherd Neame"	Square/173	12.00	15.00	8.00

SILVER STATE SPECIALITIES

DECANTERS, 1995-1998

Bear Decanters, 1995-1996

Two Hamm's Beer bears were issued for the Combined Wade/Jim Beam Show held in Seattle, Washington, USA in July 1996. They were: a (1995) "Santa's Helper Bear" re-issued in a brown and white colourway and in a limited edition of 1200; a new "Seattle 96 Bear" wearing a baseball cap, produced in a limited edition of 2000.

The "Bartender Bear" was issued in 1997 at the combined Wade/Jim Beam Fair held in Oconomowoc, Wisconsin, USA, in a limited edition of 2,000.

The "Bear in a Barrel," the last in the Hamm's Beer series, was issued in a limited edition of 1,500 and sold at the Combined Wade/Jim Beam show held in Buffalo, New York, July 1998. Buffalo is just a few miles from the World famous Niagara Falls. Commissioned by Silver State Specialities of California, this decanter was issued in a limited edition of 2,000. The original price was $25.95 U.S.

Santa's Helper   Bear Bartender   Bear in a Barrel

Backstamp **A:** "1995 Wade England S.S.S."
B: Printed "SSS Wade 1996 original 1950s Hamm's Bear"
C: Printed "Printed SSS Wade 1996"
D: Printed "1997 SSS Hamm's Bartender Bear WADE"
E: Printed "1998 SSS Hamm's Niagara Bear Wade Limited Edition 1,500"

No.	Description	Colourways	Size	U.S.$	Can.$	U.K.£
1.	Santa's Helper 1995	Black and white bear; red and white hat	120	45.00	60.00	35.00
2.	Santa's Helper 1996	Brown and white bear; red and white hat	120	45.00	60.00	35.00
3.	Seattle 1996	Black and white bear; blue cap; black lettering; "holding Hamm's. Beer" box	127	45.00	60.00	35.00
4.	Bartender 1997	Black and white bear; dark blue jacket; red tie; striped waistcoat; yellow beer glass; brown bar	125	50.00	68.00	35.00
5.	Bear in a Barrel General Issue 1998	Black and white bear; blue barrel	128	58.00	68.00	35.00
6	Bear in a Barrel Buffalo July Fair 1998	Black and white bear; brown barrel	128	58.00	68.00	40.00
7.	Bear in a Barrel Dunstable Fair October 1998	Black and white bear; green barrel	128	58.00	68.00	35.00

Black Jack Decanters, 1997

An odd playing-card shaped decanter depicting the Jack of Clubs and the Jack of Spades, commissioned by Silver State Specialities in 1997 and containing mint cordial sold for $45.00 U.S. Unfilled decanters could also be purchased.

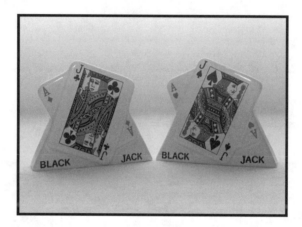

Backstamp : Printed "Genuine Wade Porcelain S.S.S. - 1997 silver paper label Silver State Mint Cordial Los Angeles, CA. 50 ml"

No.	Description	Colourways	Shape/Size	U.S.$	Can.$	U.K.£
1.	Jack of Clubs	White; multi coloured print; black lettering "Black Jack"	Triangular/115	35.00	45.00	20.00
2.	Jack of Spades	White; multi coloured print; black lettering "Black Jack"	Triangular/115	35.00	45.00	20.00

My Fair Ladies Decanters, 1992

In 1992 surplus stock of Wade's *My Fair Ladies* figurines were filled with Hebrides Scotch Whisky and sold to Silver State Specialties as whisky miniatures. The labels on the figures read "Hebrides Scotch Whisky Glasgow." A plastic seal over the whisky cork in the base prevents some models from standing upright. For original *My Fair Ladies* models, see the *Charlton Standard Catalogue of Wade, Volume One: General Issues, 5th Edition.*

Backstamp: "My Fair Ladies, fine porcelain, Wade Made in England;" model name

No.	Name	Colourways	Size	U.S.$	Can.$	U.K.£
1.	Amanda	Dark brown jacket; pink skirt; white petticoat	95	20.00	30.00	12.00
2.	Anita	Shell pink dress	90	20.00	35.00	12.00
3.	Belinda	Pearl/white/yellow dress	90	20.00	30.00	12.00
4.	Caroline	Dark blue hat; yellow flower; dark blue bodice; grey-blue skirt; yellow bow	94	20.00	30.00	12.00
5.	Diane	Pale blue/white hat, jacket, handbag; off-white skirt	90	20.00	30.00	12.00
6.	Emma	White dress; creamy yellow shawl, ribbons, bows	90	20.00	30.00	12.00
7.	Hannah	Brown hair; green/grey/white dress	94	20.00	30.00	12.00
8.	Kate	Grey hat; off-white/grey dress; red roses	96	20.00	30.00	12.00
9.	Lisa	Brown hair; pastel blue/white dress	94	20.00	30.00	12.00
10.	Lucy	Grey hat, skirt; dark brown jacket, handbag	90	20.00	30.00	12.00
11.	Marie	Dark green hat; dark green/grey-green dress	92	20.00	30.00	12.00
12	Melissa	Light brown hat; dark blue jacket; pale blue skirt; white petticoat	95	20.00	30.00	12.00
13.	Natalie	Pale pink dress; light grey shawl, ribbons, bows	90	20.00	30.00	12.00
14.	Rachel	White/grey-blue dress; grey-blue hat	96	20.00	30.00	12.00
15.	Rebecca	Yellow/beige hat; pink flower; grey bodice; white skirt; pink bow	94	20.00	30.00	12.00
16.	Sarah	Greenish grey hat; greenish grey/white dress; pink flowers	92	20.00	30.00	12.00

SALT AND PEPPER, 1999

The salt and pepper set are Hamm's Beer Bears. They were produced in a limited edition of five hundred. Four hundred pairs have the U.S. flag on the back and one hundred pairs have the British Union Jack flag on the back.

No.	Description	Colourways	Shape/Size	U.S.$	Can.$	U.K.£
1.	Pepper	Black/white; red lettering "Hamm's Beer"	85	Unknown		
2.	Salt	Brown/white; red lettering "Hamm's Beer"	85	Unknown		

SKOL LAGER

ASHTRAYS

Backstamp : Printed "Wade pdm England" (pdm separated 1984-1990)

No.	Description	Colourways	Shape/Size	U.S.$	Can.$	U.K.£
1.	Ashtray	White; black/gold line; red lettering "SKOL"	Square / 185	10.00	12.00	6.00
2.	Ashtray	White; black/gold line; red lettering "SKOL"	Square / 155	10.00	12.00	6.00

SMIRNOFF VODKA

DRINK POURERS AND TANKARD, c.1970-1992

These pourers, shape C53, have a straight base and are found with a metal tube and spout. The issue date of the tankard is unknown. The print on the tankard is of the Smirnoff Vodka label.

Drink Pourer (No.1)

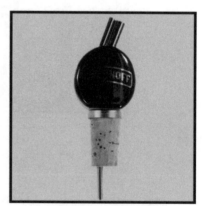

Drink Pourer (No.3)

Backstamp: "Wade Regicor Made in UK"

No.	Description	Colourways	Shape/Size	U.S.$	Can.$	U.K.£
1.	Drink Pourer	White; yellow crown; red lettering "Smirnoff Vodka"	Circular/41	30.00	35.00	15.00
2.	Drink Pourer	White; multi-coloured lettering "Smirnoff"	Circular/41	30.00	35.00	15.00
3.	Drink Pourer	Black; metal spout & neck; gold lettering "Smirnoff"	C53/41 x 44 Round	25.00	30.00	10.00
4.	Tankard	Black; red/gold label	Pint/115	10.00	15.00	5.00

SPEY ROYAL

WATER JUG

Backstamp : Printed "Wade pdm England" (pdm separated 1984-1990)

No.	Description	Colourways	Shape/Size	U.S.$	Can.$	U.K.£
1.	Water Jug, ice-check spout	Black; maroon label; white/gold lettering "SPR Spey Royal Fine Old Scotch Whisky"	140 Rectangular	35.00	40.00	20.00

SPRINGBANK WHISKY

WATER JUGS, 1969-1984

This water jug has an open spout.

Water Jug (No.2)

Backstamp: Printed "Wade pdm England" (pdm joined 1969-1984)

No.	Description	Colourways	Shape/Size	U.S.$	Can.$	U.K.œ
1.	Water Jug	Black; gold/white lettering "Springbank Whisky"	Round/153	30.00	35.00	15.00
2.	Water Jug	Black; white/gold lettering "Springbank Campbeltown Malt Scotch Whisky"	Round/153	30.00	35.00	15.00

STAR BEERS

WATER JUG, 1960-1962

This jug has a recessed handle and open spout. It is decorated with a print of a town crier.

Photograph not available
at press time

Backstamp: "Wade Regicor, London England," laurel leaves, large size

No.	Description	Colourways	Shape/Size	U.S.$	Can.$	U.K.£
1.	Water Jug	White; black/red print; black lettering "Star Beers Brightest and Best since 1777"	Round/102	30.00	35.00	15.00

STEIN LAGER

BAR LAMP, 1969-1984

This triangular shaped "Bar Lamp" would have been produced for use in public houses or hotels in England that sold Stein Lager.

Backstamp : Green printed "Wade pdm" (pdm joined 1969-1984)

No.	Description	Colourways	Shape/Size	U.S.$	Can.$	U.K.£
1.	Bar Lamp	White; grey/orange print of a Stein; blue/yellow lettering "Stein The Great Gold Lager"	135	50.00	70.00	35.00

STONES BITTER

COUNTER DISPLAY AND WATER JUGS, 1968-1995

The counter display was issued between 1968 and 1984, the water jugs between 1990 and 1995.

Counter Display

Water Jug (No.3)

Backstamp: **A:** "Wade pdm England"
B: "Wade P D M Made in England"
C: Transfer print "Wade pdm England" (pdm joined 1969-1984)

No.	Description	Colourways	Shape/Size	U.S.$	Can.$	U.K.£
1.	Counter Display	Dull yellow; gold/black print; red/black lettering "Stones Best Bitter"	Rectangular/210	25.00	30.00	12.00
2.	Water Jug, open spout	Yellow; white/red lettering "Stones Best Bitter"	Rectangular/133	15.00	20.00	8.00
3.	Water Jug, open Spout	Yellow tan; white label; red band; red/black lettering "Stones Best Bitter"	Rectangular/152	30.00	35.00	12.00

STONE'S GINGER WINE

DRINK POURERS

Drink Pourer (No.1)   Drink Pourer (No.2)

Backstamp: Impressed "5455/1" on underside of button

No.	Description	Colourways	Shape/Size	U.S.$	Can.$	U.K.£
1.	Drink Pourer	White/dark green; metal spout, neck; white lettering "Stone's"	5455/1 40 x 47 Octagonal	25.00	30.00	12.00
2.	Drink Pourer	White/dark green; plastic spout, neck white lettering "Stone's"	5455/1 40 x 47 Octagonal	20.00	25.00	10.00

STOWELLS OF CHELSEA WINE SELLERS

DRINK POURER

This drink pourer, shape C53, has a straight base.

Photograph not available
at press time

Backstamp: Unmarked

No.	Description	Colourways	Shape/Size	U.S.$	Can.$	U.K.£
1.	Drink Pourer	White; plastic tube; blue lettering "Stowells of Chelsea"	Circular/41	38.00	50.00	15.00

STRATHSPEY HIGHLAND MALT SCOTCH WHISKY

DRINK POURER

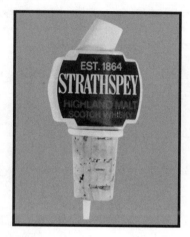

Backstamp: Impressed "C52A" under porcelain button, not seen unless pourer is taken apart

No.	Description	Colourways	Shape/size	U.S.$	Can.$	U.K.£
1.	Drink Pourer	White/black; plastic spout, neck; lettering "Est. 1864 Strathspey Highland Malt Scotch Whisky"	C52A/40 x 48 Octagonal	25.00	30.00	12.00

STRONGBOW CIDER

ASHTRAY, 1969-1984

Backstamp: "Wade pdm England"

No.	Description	Colourways	Size	U.S.$	Can.$	U.K.£
1.	Ashtray	Black; white print; yellow lettering "Strongbow"	175	45.00	55.00	25.00

TANQUERAY ENGLISH GIN

ASHTRAY AND WATER JUG, 1969-1990

The ashtray was produced between 1984 and 1990 and the water jug between 1969 and 1984. The pourers, shape number C52A, have a notched base and shoulders. They were produced with plastic tubes.

Ashtray

Water Jug

Backstamp: **A:** "Wade p d m England"
B: "Wade pdm England, Imported by the Buckingham Corporation New York. NY. Distilled Blended and Bottled in Scotland 86 Proof"

No.	Description	Colourways	Shape/Size	U.S.$	Can.$	U.K.£
1.	Ashtray	Green; black lettering "Tanqueray English Gin"	Oval/177	10.00	15.00	5.00
2.	Water Jug, ice-check spout	Dark green; white label; red/black lettering "Tanqueray Special Dry"	Round/177	25.00	30.00	12.00

DRINK POURERS

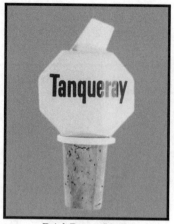

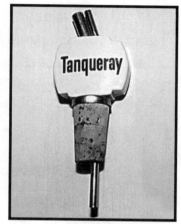

Drink Pourer (No.2)   Drink Pourer (No.3)

Backstamp A: Impressed "C52A" under porcelain button, seen when pourer is taken apart
B: Impressed "5455/1" on underside of button

No.	Description	Colourways	Shape/Size	U.S.$	Can.$	U.K.£
1.	Drink Pourer	White; metal spout, neck; dark green lettering "Tanqueray"	C52A/40 x 48 Octagonal	25.00	30.00	12.00
2.	Drink Pourer	White; plastic spout, neck; dark green lettering "Tanqueray"	5455/1 40 x 47 Octagonal	25.00	30.00	12.00
3.	Drink Pourer	White; dark green lettering "Tanqueray"	Square/38	30.00	35.00	15.00
4.	Drink Pourer	Yellow; black lettering "Tanqueray"	Square/38	30.00	35.00	15.00

TAPLOWS

DRINK POURER

No.	Description	Colourways	Shape/Size	U.S.$	Can.$	U.K.£
1.	Drink Pourer	White; red/black print; metal spout, neck; black lettering "Taplows"	C62 / 47 x 41 Rectangular	30.00	35.00	12.00

TAUNTON CIDER PLC

BAR SNACK DISH

Backstamp: Unknown

No.	Description	Colourways	Shape/size	U.S.$	Can.$	U.K.£
1.	Snack Dish	Brown; gold line, lettering "Taunton Cider"	Round/235	12.00	18.00	8.00

BAR LAMP

On the front of this "Cider Jug Lamp" is a black transfer print of two men and two horses turning a cider press. The lamp shade is white with a brown band around the rim, bearing the words "Taunton Cider" in large white letters.

No.	Description	Colourways	Size	U.S.$	Can.$	U.K.£
1.	Cider Jug Lamp	Dark brown/off-white jug; black print, lettering	210	60.00	80.00	30.00

JUGS, c.1985

These jugs, with a flat outer edge on the handle, were used on pub bars as advertising pieces and contained no cider. They were produced with various labels on the fronts which advertised Taunton products. No. 4 has a circular plastic label on the front and stands on a base bearing the words "Made by Taunton Cider Co Ltd."

Bar Display Jug

This pottery cider jug was produced as a display piece and has a section cut out of the back for a clamp to fasten to a bar top.

Backstamp: None

No.	Description	Colourways	Shape/Size	U.S.$	Can.$	U.K.£
1.	Cider Jug Display	Amber/white; black label; black/gold	Round/165		Unknown	

Cider Jugs

Small and Large Jug (No.1, No.5)

Small Jug (No.3)

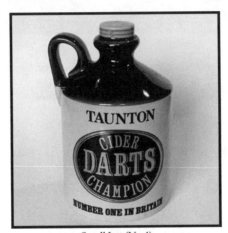

Small Jug (No.4)

Backstamp: Unmarked

No.	Description	Colourways	Size	U.S.$	Can.$	U.K.£
1.	Cider Jug	Dark brown/red; black/yellow/white label "Autumn Gold Premium Cider"	Small/159	40.00	45.00	20.00
2.	Cider Jug	Dark brown/off white; black/white/gold label "Dry Blackthorn Cooled on Draught"	Small/159	40.00	45.00	20.00
3.	Cider Jug	Dark brown/off white; black/gold label "Cider Darts Champion Number One in Britain"	Small/159	50.00	70.00	25.00
4.	Cider Jug	Dark brown/off white; black/white/yellow plastic label "Dry Blackthorn Cider;" brown plastic stand	Small/159	50.00	70.00	25.00
5.	Cider Jug	Dark brown/red; black/yellow/white label "Autumn Gold Premium Cider"	Large/210	70.00	90.00	35.00
6.	Cider Jug	Dark brown/off white; black/white/gold label "Dry Blackthorn Cooled on Draught"	Large/210	70.00	90.00	35.00
7.	Cider Jug	Dark brown/off white; black/yellow/gold label "Dry Blackthorn Cooled on Draught"	Large/210	70.00	90.00	35.00

LOVING CUPS

The Taunton Cider Company has a large collection of early 19thcentury cider mugs and loving cups. Starting in 1973, Wade was given the task of reproducing some of the original designs onto loving cups and mugs. All the miniature loving cups were issued in pairs.

Apples and Blossom, 1986

"Apples and Blossom"

Backstamp: "A limited number of these traditional Cider Mugs were produced by Wade Potteries for the Taunton Cider Company"

No.	Description	Colourways	Size	U.S.$	Can.$	U.K.£
1.	1986 Loving Cup	White; green leaves; red apples; white blossoms	½ pint/83	85.00	100.00	45.00

Apples and Leaves, 1985

This loving cup has bands of apple leaves printed around the inside rim and a garland of leaves around the centre design of apples.

Photograph not available
at press time

Backstamp: "500 of these Traditional Cider Mugs were reproduced by Wade Potteries For the Taunton Cider Company 1985"

No.	Description	Colourways	Size	U.S.$	Can.$	U.K.£
1.	1985 Loving Cup	White; red/green print	½ pint/83	85.00	100.00	45.00

Apples and Leaves (Five), 1981

On the front and back of this loving cup are the words "Taunton Cider" with a print of five apples and leaves. A print of bunches of green leaves decorate the handles and inside the cup.

"Apples and Leaves"

Backstamp: "A limited number of these traditional Cider Mugs were produced by Wade Potteries for the Taunton Cider Company 1981"

No.	Description	Colourways	Size	U.S.$	Can.$	U.K.£
1.	1981 Loving Cup	White; green leaves; red apples; white blossom	½ pint/83	85.00	100.00	45.00

Arthur Moore-Blackthorn Cider, 1980

The half-pint loving cup has the story of Arthur Moore, the founder of the Taunton Cider Company, printed on the back.

"Arthur Moore-Blackthom Cider Label"

Backstamp: "Wade pdm England"

No.	Description	Colourways	Size	U.S.$	Can.$	U.K.£
1.	1980 Loving Cup	White; black/white label, lettering "Taunton Dry Blackthorn Cider"	½ pint/85	60.00	80.00	40.00
2.	1980 Loving Cup	White; black/white label, lettering "Taunton Dry Blackthorn Cider"	Pint/120	65.00	85.00	42.00

258

Autumn Gold Cider Press, 1980, 1987

These loving cups have a transfer print on both sides showing men working on the 19th-century Taunton Mill cider presses, with the words "Presented by The Taunton Cider Company." Cup No.2 has plain handles, cup No.1 has prints on the handle only and cup No.3 (miniature) has an apples and leaves print on the handles and on the inside rim.

No print on handles, left; print on handles, right

Loving Cup, Miniature

Backstamp: A: "Wade pdm England"
B: "Pair of 500 of these Traditional Cider Mugs were produced in miniature by Wade Potteries For the Taunton Cider Company 1987"
C: Printed "Special Edition Cider Mug by Wade Potteries Staffordshire"

No.	Description	Colourways	Size	U.S.$	Can.$	U.K.£
1.	1980 Loving Cup	White; black print, plain handles	½ pint/83	90.00	100.00	45.00
2.	1980 Loving Cup	White; black print, prints on handles	½ pint/83	95.00	105.00	50.00
3.	1987 Loving Cup	White; black print, prints on handles and inside rim	Miniature/65	75.00	85.00	40.00

British Darts and Euchre Champions, 1981

These loving cups were produced for the British Dart Championships and the British Euchre Championships in 1981. The print is of a large *T* surrounded by apples.

Photograph not available
at press time

Backstamp: "A limited number of these traditional Cider Mugs were produced by Wade Potteries for the Taunton Cider Company"

No.	Description	Colourways	Size	U.S.$	Can.$	U.K.£
1.	1981 Loving Cup	Beige; black print, lettering "Taunton Cider British Darts Championship 1981"	Pint/120	80.00	90.00	40.00
2.	1981 Loving Cup	Beige; black lettering "Taunton British Euchre Championship"	Pint/120	80.00	90.00	40.00

Chinese Rose/Chinoiserie Japonika, 1984

This decoration on this loving cup is also known as "Chinoiserie Japonika."

Backstamp: Red printed "500 of these Traditional Cider Mugs were reproduced by Wade Potteries for the Tuanton Cider Company 1984"

No.	Description	Colourways	Shape/Size	U.S.$	Can.$	U.K.£
1.	1984 Loving Cup	White; pale pink/blue flowers; green leaves	Quart/130	105.00	140.00	65.00

Fans and Flowers Loving Cup, 1996

Backstamp: Green printed "This mug is one of a limited edition of five hundred specially commissioned by Matthew Clark Taunton. It is copied from a 19th century original in the Matthew Clark Taunton Collection 1996 WADE"

No..	Description	Colourways	Shape/Size	U.S.$	Can.$	U.K.£
1.	1996 Loving Cup	White; green fans and leaves; dark red and yellow flowers	Pint/120	85.00	120.00	55.00

Girl with Goat, 1976-1977

The quart loving cup was produced in 1976, and the miniature was issued in 1977.

"Girl with a Goat"

Backstamp: A: "500 of these Traditional Cider Mugs were reproduced by Wade Potteries for the Taunton Cider Company 1976"
B: "500 pairs of these Traditional Cider Mugs were Produced in Miniature by Wade Potteries for the Taunton Cider Company 1977"

No.	Description	Colourways	Size	U.S.$	Can.$	U.K.£
1.	1976 Loving Cup	White; black/yellow/red print	Quart/135	110.00	145.00	65.00
2.	1977 Loving Cup	White; black/yellow/red print	Miniature/65	60.00	80.00	35.00

"God Speed The Plough" Loving Cups, 1973-1975, 1981

"1973 Good Speed the Plough"

"1974 God Speed the Plough"

"1981 God Speed the Plough"

"God Speed the Plough"

Backstamp: A: "500 of these Traditional Cider Mugs were reproduced by Wade Potteries for the Taunton Cider Company 1973"
B: "500 of these Traditional Cider Mugs were reproduced by Wade Potteries for the Taunton Cider Company 1974"
C: "Royal Victoria Pottery Staffordshire, Wade England"
D: "500 pairs of these Traditional Cider Mugs were produced in miniature by Wade Potteries for the Taunton Cider Company 1981"

No.	Description	Colourways	Size	U.S.$	Can.$	U.K.£
1.	1973 Loving Cup	White; black/brown print	Quart/120	110.00	145.00	65.00
2.	1974 Loving Cup	White; multi-coloured print	½ pint/83	110.00	145.00	65.00
3.	1975 Loving Cup	White; multi-coloured print	Miniature/65	60.00	80.00	35.00
4.	1981 Loving Cup	White; black/brown print	Miniature/65	60.00	80.00	35.00

Holly Leaves, 1994

Holly leaves and berries decorate this loving cup.

Photograph not available
at press time

Backstamp: "This Mug is one of five hundred specially commissioned by Taunton Cider. It is reproduced from a 19th century presentation original. 1994 Wade"

No.	Description	Colourways	Size	U.S.$	Can.$	U.K.£
1.	1994 Loving Cup	White; green/red/gold leaves	Pint/120	85.00	120.00	55.00

Home Place, 1987

"1987 The Home Place"

Backstamp: "A limited edition of this Traditional Cider Mug was reproduced for Taunton Cider by Wade Potteries, Staffordshire"

No.	Description	Colourways	Size	U.S.$	Can.$	U.K.£
1.	1987 Loving Cup	White; multi-coloured print	½ pint/83	55.00	70.00	30.00

19th Century Floral Design, 1983

The print on this cup is of flowers and leaves.

Photograph not available
at press time

Backstamp: "This Mug is one of a limited edition of five hundred specially commissioned by Taunton Cider. It is produced from a 19th Century original in the Taunton Cider collection 1983 Wade"

No.	Description	Colourways	Size	U.S.$	Can.$	U.K.£
1.	1983 Loving Cup	White; deep red/white flowers; green/yellow/grey leaves; gold/blue rim	Quart/130	85.00	120.00	55.00

19th *Century Floral Design, 1988*

This cup is decorated with a 19thcentury floral design.

Photograph not available
at press time

Backstamp: "A Limited edition of this Traditional Cider Mug was reproduced for Taunton Cider by Wade Potteries Staffordshire"

No.	Description	Colourways	Size	U.S.$	Can.$	U.K.£
1.	1988 Loving Cup	White; black rim, base, handles; multi-coloured flowers	Pint/120	110.00	145.00	65.00

Pastel Garden, 1992

"Pastel Garden"

Backstamp: "This Mug is one of a limited edition of five hundred specially commissioned by Taunton Cider. It is produced from a 19th Century original in the Taunton Cider collection, 1992 Wade"

No.	Description	Colourways	Size	U.S.$	Can.$	U.K.£
1.	1992 Loving Cup	Pastel green; pink blossom; light brown leaves	Pint/120	125.00	165.00	80.00
2.	1992 Loving Cup	Pastel green; pink blossom; light brown leaves	½ pint/90	110.00	145.00	65.00

Peonies and Swallow, 1991

The Chinese-style print on this cup is of large peonies and a bird on a tree branch."Taunton Cider May 1991" is printed around the base.

Photograph not available
at press time

Backstamp: "This mug is one of a limited edition of five hundred specially commissioned by Taunton Cider. It is produced from a 19th Century original in the Taunton Cider collection, 1991 Wade"

No.	Description	Colourways	Size	U.S.$	Can.$	U.K.£
1.	1991 Loving Cup	White; gold rim; blue/red/yellow/pink flowers, bird	120	110.00	145.00	65.00

Somerset Hunt Master of Hounds, 1975

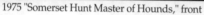

1975 "Somerset Hunt Master of Hounds," front

1975 "Somerset Hunt Master of Hounds," back

Backstamp: "500 of these Traditional Cider Mugs were reproduced by Wade Potteries For the Taunton Cider Company 1975"

No.	Description	Colourways	Size	U.S.$	Can.$	U.K.£
1.	1975 Loving Cup	White; multi-coloured print	Pint/125	125.00	165.00	80.00

Note: See *The Charlton Standard Catalogue of Wade Volume One; General Issues, 5th Edition* for the 1977 Silver Jubilee Loving Cup.

Spitting Frog, 1995

This loving cup has a model of a spitting frog inside the cup. A blackberry print decorates the outside.

Photograph not available
at press time

Backstamp: "This Frog mug is one of a limited edition of five hundred specially commissioned by Taunton Cider. It is copied from a 19th century original in the Taunton Cider Collection. 1995 Wade PDM. Made in England"

No.	Description	Colourways	Size	U.S.$	Can.$	U.K.£
1.	1995 Loving Cup	White; blue berries; light brown frog	Quart/120	85.00	120.00	55.00

Spring Flowers, 1990

A single transfer print of spring flowers, illustrated in the 19th century style, is on this cup.

"Spring Flowers"

Backstamp: "500 of these traditional cider mugs were reproduced by Wade Potteries for the Taunton Cider Company 1990"

No.	Description	Colourways	Size	U.S.$	Can.$	U.K.£
1.	1990 Loving Cup	White; black print	Pint/120	85.00	120.00	55.00

T Logo

"Taunton Cider" Loving Cup

"Taunton Tradition Draught" Loving Cup

Backstamp: "Wade pdm England"

No.	Description	Colourways	Size	U.S.$	Can.$	U.K.£
1.	Loving Cup	White cup; orange apples; black lettering "Taunton Cider"	½ pint/83	60.00	80.00	40.00
2.	Loving Cup	White; orange apples, red/black lettering "Taunton Traditional Draught"	Quart/140	60.00	80.00	40.00

Taunton Cider Story, 1978-1979

This loving cup has a large *T* on the front, with a cascade of apples on each side, and the words "The Taunton Cider Company." A print of a thatched-roof cottage is on the back with the story of Taunton Cider.

"Taunton Cider Story"

Backstamp: A. "A limited edition of 4,000 produced for the Taunton Cider Company by Wade Heath Potteries Staffordshire in the year of 1978"
B. "A limited edition of 4,000 produced for the Taunton Cider Company by Wade Heath Potteries Staffordshire in the year of 1979"

No.	Description	Colourways	Size	U.S.$	Can.$	U.K.£
1.	1978 Loving Cup	White; red T; orange/red apples; yellow print	½ pint/85	85.00	120.00	55.00
2.	1979 Loving Cup	White; red T; orange/red apples; yellow print	½ pint/85	85.00	120.00	55.00

Three-Handled Loving Cup, 1978

The three handles of this unusual loving cup are edged with gold. There is a spray of flowers between each handle.

"Three-Handled Loving Cup"

Backstamp: "500 of these Traditional Cider Mugs were reproduced by Wade Potteries For the Taunton Cider Company 1978"

No.	Description	Colourways	Size	U.S.$	Can.$	U.K.£
1.	1978 Loving Cup	White; gold rim, base, handles; multi-coloured flowers	Pint/120	100.00	145.00	65.00

Views of Taunton, 1974, 1982

Views of Taunton quart and miniature loving cups

Backstamp: A. "500 of these Traditional Cider Mugs were reproduced by Wade Potteries For the Taunton Cider Company 1974"
B. "This Mug is one of a limited edition of five hundred specially commissioned by Taunton Cider. It is produced from a 19th Century original in the Taunton Cider collection 1974 Wade"
C. "500 pairs of these Traditional Cider Mugs were produced in miniature by Wade Potteries For the Taunton Cider Company 1982"

No.	Description	Colourways	Size	U.S.$	Can.$	U.K.£
1.	1974 Loving Cup	White; blue print	Quart/130	125.00	165.00	80.00
2.	1974 Loving Cup	White; blue print	Pint/120	110.00	145.00	65.00
3.	1982 Loving Cup	White; blue print	Miniature/65	60.00	80.00	55.00

The Wassailing Story, 1987

A transfer print of men firing guns into an orchard is on the front of this loving cup and the history of Wassailing on the reverse with the following words: "Taunton Cider keeps alive the tradition of Wassailing the apple trees. Each year Taunton sponsors this event, in which the trees are annointed with honey and bread to assure a good harvest."

"The Wassailing Story"

Backstamp: "Produced exclusively for the Taunton Cider Company by Wade Potteries of Staffordshire"

No.	Description	Colourways	Size	U.S.$	Can.$	U.K.£
1.	1987 Loving Cup	Cream; brown print	½ pint/83	80.00	100.00	45.00

MUGS

Chain of Flowers, 1977

"Chain of Flowers"

Backstamp: "500 of these traditional Cider Mugs were reproduced by Wade Potteries for the Taunton Cider Company 1977"

No.	Description	Colourways	Size	U.S.$	Can.$	U.K.£
1.	1977 Mug	White; multi-coloured flowers	Pint/105	100.00	135.00	60.00

Christmas Rose, Wavy Rim, 1985

The large white flower on this mug resembles a Christmas Rose.

"Christmas Rose"

Backstamp: Blue printed "500 of these traditional Cider mugs were reproduced by Wade Potteries for the Taunton Cider Company 1985"

No.	Description	Colourways	Size	U.S.$	Can.$	U.K.£
1.	Wavy Rim Floral Mug	White; multi coloured flowers print	125	90.00	120.00	55.00

Floral Rim, Ribbed Body, 1979

This pretty ribbed-body mug with tapered sides has the floral decoration around the outside and inside the rim. There is gold highlighting on the rim, handle and base.

"Floral Rim"

Backstamp: Black printed "500 of these traditional Cider mugs were reproduced by Wade Potteries for the Taunton Cider Company 1979"

No.	Description	Colourways	Size	U.S.$	Can.$	U.K.£
1.	Floral Mug	White; gold highlights; pale yellow/orange flowers; dark blue/green leaves	125	90.00	120.00	55.00

Floral Trees, 1980

An ornate design of flowers and trees was printed on this mug.

Photograph not available
at press time

Backstamp: "This Mug is one of a limited edition of five hundred specially commissioned by Taunton Cider. It is produced from a 19th Century original in the Taunton Cider collection 1980 Wade"

No.	Description	Colourways	Size	U.S.$	Can.$	U.K.£
1.	1980 Mug	White; red-brown/black print	Pint/120	100.00	135.00	60.00

Ladies With Parasols in Garden, 1989

An 19th century scene of ladies with parasols walking under a bower of trees decorates this mug.

Photograph not available
at press time

Backstamp: "500 of these traditional cider mugs were reproduced by Wade Potteres for the Taunton Cider Company 1980"

No.	Description	Colourways	Size	U.S.$	Can.$	U.K.£
1.	1989 Mug	White; blue print	Pint/120	80.00	100.00	40.00

The Miller, 1977

"The Miller"

Backstamp: "500 of these tradition Cider Mugs were reproduced by Wade Potteries for the Taunton Cider Company 1977"

No.	Description	Colourways	Size	U.S.$	Can.$	U.K.£
1.	1977 Mug	White; black print	Pint/105	100.00	135.00	60.00

Orange Flower Tapered Mug, 1987

The large orange flower on this mug resembles a poppy.

"Orange Flower"

Backstamp: Printed "500 of these Traditional Cider Mugs were reproduced by Wade Potteries For the Taunton Cider Company 1987"

No.	Description	Colourways	Size	U.S.$	Can.$	U.K.£
1.	Orange Flowered Mug	White; orange flowers; dark brown, brown and green leaves	100	90.00	120.00	55.00

Stock Exchange Floral, 1992

This mug is decorated with a gold-leaf design. It was produced to commemorate the listing of Taunton Cider on the stock exchange on July 23, 1992, and was presented to Taunton employees.

Photograph not available
at press time

Backstamp: "A limited edition drinking Mug copied from an original, dating from 1820, which is held in the Taunton Cider Collection. This mug was produced to Commemorate Taunton Ciders Listing on the Stock Exchange, 23rd July 1992, Wade No. 20"

No.	Description	Colourways	Size	U.S.$	Can.$	U.K.£
1.	1992 Mug	Navy blue; gold decoration	Pint/120	150.00	200.00	80.00

"T", 1973-1974

"T" Mug

Backstamp: "Wade pdm England"

No.	Description	Colourways	Size	U.S.$	Can.$	U.K.£
1.	Mug	Pink; black apples	Miniature /63	55.00	75.00	35.00
2.	Mug	Yellow; red/orange apples	½ pint/83	55.00	75.00	35.00

Victorian Sporting Scenes, 1993

Victorian scenes of cricket and soccer players are printed on this mug.

Photograph not available
at press time

Backstamp: "This mug is one of a limited edition of five hundred specially commissioned by Taunton Cider. It is produced from a 19th century original in the Taunton Cider Collection. 1993 Wade"

No.	Description	Colourways	Size	U.S.$	Can.$	U.K.£
1.	1993 Mug	White; pink print	Quart/120	90.00	120.00	55.00

PUMP HANDLES, 1970s

Beer-pump handles were produced by Wade PDM for Taunton, which installed them in the public houses that served their draught ciders.

Pump handle (No.1), Pump handle (No.2)

Backstamp: Unmarked

No.	Description	Colourways	Size	U.S.$	Can.$	U.K.£
1.	Pump Handles	Brown; multi-coloured lettering "Taunton Traditional Draught Cider"	170	38.00	50.00	15.00
2.	Pump Handles	White; red/multi-coloured lettering "Taunton T"	225	30.00	35.00	15.00

TEACHER'S SCOTCH WHISKY

ASHTRAYS AND WATER JUGS, 1984-1990

Ashtray (No.2)

Water jug (No.3)

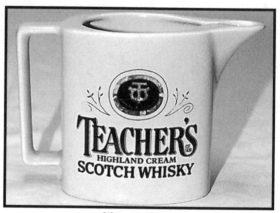

Water jug (No.4)

Backstamp: A. "Wade pdm England"
B. "Wade p d m England"

No.	Description	Colourways	Shape/Size	U.S.$	Can.$	U.K.£
1.	Ashtray	Yellow; black print, lettering "Teacher's Highland Cream"	Round/153	10.00	15.00	5.00
2.	Ashtray	White; gold lettering "Teacher's Highland Cream Scotch Whisky"	Square/90	10.00	12.00	8.00
3.	Water Jug, ice-check spout	Black; gold lettering "Teacher's Scotch Whisky in a class of its own"	Round/127	28.00	35.00	22.00
4.	Water Jug, ice-check spout	Cream; gold logo; black lettering "Teacher's Highland Cream Scotch Whisky"	Round/133	28.00	35.00	22.00
5.	Water Jug, open spout	Black; gold lettering "Teacher's Scotch Whisky"	Square/125	28.00	35.00	22.00

TENNANTS

ASHTRAYS, 1955-1990

Ashtray (No.1)

Ashtray (No.6)

Backstamp: A. "Wade Regicor, London England," laurel leaves, large size
B. "Wade pdm England"
C. "Wade p d m England"

No.	Description	Colourways	Shape/Size	U.S.$	Can.$	U.K.£
1.	Ashtray	White/dark green band; multi-coloured label, lettering "Tennants Gold Label Sparkling Barley Wine"	Round/140	15.00	20.00	8.00
2.	Ashtray	Green/white; multi-coloured label, lettering "Tennants Gold Label Sparkling Barley Wine"	Round/140	15.00	20.00	8.00
3.	Ashtray	White; multi-coloured label, lettering "Tennants Gold Label Sparkling Barley Wine"	Square/140	15.00	20.00	8.00
4.	Ashtray	Red; white lettering "Tennants Best Bitter"	Square/140	15.00	20.00	8.00
5.	Ashtray	Black; red lettering "Tennants Extra"	Square/140	15.00	20.00	8.00
6.	Ashtray	White; red/black lettering "Tennants Glucose Stout for Vitality Plus"	Square/146	15.00	20.00	8.00
7.	Ashtray	White; red band; multi-coloured label "Tennants Gold Label Sparkling Barley Wine"	Round/140	15.00	20.00	8.00
8.	Ashtray	White; yellow band; multi-coloured label "Tennants Gold Label Sparkling Barley Wine"	Round/140	15.00	20.00	8.00

BAR LAMP

The cardboard/cloth covered shade on this square based lamp has the name Tennants around it. There are vents around the shade which allow the heat from the light bulb to escape sideways, making the shade revolve.

Photograph not available
at press time

Backstamp: Printed "Wade pdm England" (pdm joined 1969-1984)

No.	Description	Colourways	Size	U.S.$	Can.$	U.K.£
1.	Bar Lamp	Dark blue base; white lettering; buff coloured shade; brown lettering	310 x 125	80.00	100.00	40.00

TENNENT'S LAGER

ASHTRAYS, 1969-1995

Ashtray (No.1)

Ashtray (No.2))

Backstamp: **A**. "Wade pdm England"
B. "Wade p d m England"
C. "Wade P D M Made in England"
D. Red printed "Wade pdm England" (pdm separated 1984-1990)

No.	Description	Colourways	Shape/Size	U.S.$	Can.$	U.K.£
1.	Ashtray	Black; white/yellow lettering "Tennent's Extra Export Lager"	Square/177	10.00	15.00	5.00
2.	Ashtray	Black; white lettering "Tennent's Lager"	Square/177	10.00	15.00	5.00
3.	Ashtray	Maroon tray/print; cream label; white lettering "Tennent's 80/-"	Square/153	12.00	15.00	8.00

BAR LAMPS

Bar Lamp (No.1)

Bar Lamp (No.2)

Backstamp: Printed "Wade - Regicor London England," in laurel leaf frame (small size 13 x 13mm 1962-late 1968)

No.	Description	Colourways	Shape/Size	U.S.$	Can.$	U.K.£
1.	Bar Lamp	Base: Pale blue; red print T and white lettering "Trade Mark"	Cube/185	60.00	80.00	45.00
2.	Bar Lamp	Base: Dark blue; white lettering "Tennent's lager;" Shade: red T and white lettering "Tennent's Lager"	Rectangular/115	60.00	80.00	45.00

BAR SNACK DISH

Backstamp: Printed "Wade Regicor London England," laurel leaf frame (large size 18 x 20mm 1953-1962)

No.	Description	Colourways	Shape/size	U.S.$	Can.$	U.K.£
1.	Snack dish	Pale blue; red "T" Trade Mark; blue lettering "Tennent's Lager"	Round / 242	35.00	40.00	20.00

SALT AND PEPPER

Backstamp: Red printed "Wade England"

No.	Description	Colourways	Shape/Size	U.S.$	Can.$	U.K.£
1.	Salt/Pepper	White; blue lettering; red "T" "Tennent's lager"	Rectangular / 117	10.00	15.00	8.00

WATER JUGS

Water Jug (No.4)

Water Jug (No.6)

Water Jug (No.7)

No.	Description	Colourways	Shape/Size	U.S.$	Can.$	U.K.£
1.	Water Jug	White; blue/red lettering "Tennent's Lager"	Rectangular/114	25.00	30.00	12.00
2.	Water Jug	White; red/blue lettering "Lots of Tennent's Lager"	Rectangular/140	25.00	30.00	12.00
3.	Water Jug	White; red/black lettering "T Tennent's Lager"	Round/165	25.00	30.00	12.00
4.	Water Jug	Royal blue; white lettering "Tennent's Lager"	Square/114	25.00	30.00	12.00

TETLEY ALES
CARLSBEG-TETLEY

BAR SNACK DISH, 1984-1990

Ashtray (No.2)

Backstamp: **A.** "Wade p d m England"
B. Black transfer print "Wade pdm England" (pdm joined 1969-1984)

No.	Description	Colourways	Shape/Size	U.S.$	Can.$	U.K.£
1.	Dish	Yellow; red lettering "Tetley Ales"	Round/195	10.00	15.00	5.00
2.	Dish	Black; white lettering "Tetley Bittermen. You Can't Beat 'em. Join 'em"	Round/140	10.00	14.00	6.00

MENU HOLDERS

Used for holding menu of bar meals in British pubs, this menu holder has a print of a Huntsman holding a pint of Tetley Ale.

Backstamp: Embossed "S25/66"

No.	Description	Colourways	Shape/Size	U.S.$	Can.$	U.K.£
1.	Menu Holder	White; red/black print & lettering "Tetley"	Square/45	40.00	50.00	25.00
2.	Menu Holder	Black; white lettering "Tetley Bittermen"	48 x 60/ Rectangular	30.00	40.00	20.00

STEINS

This stein has a portrait with the words Joshua Tetley & Son on the front, and Joshua Tetley July 20th 1778 -August 26th 1859 Founder of the firm of Joshua Tetley & Son Ltd on the back. A similar stein has also been reported that has the words "Joshua Tetley a Leeds Maltster purchased a Salem, Brewery in 1822" added to the "Joshua Tetley Founder" inscription.

Joshua Tetley & Son (front)

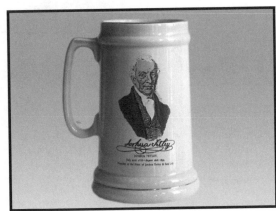
Joshua Tetley & Son (back)

Backstamp: Red Printed "Wade pdm England" (pdm separated 1984-1990)

No.	Description	Colourways	Size	U.S.$	Can.$	U.K.£
1.	Stein	White; gold bands; multi coloured prints "Joshua Tetley Founder"	177	20.00	30.00	15.00
2.	Stein	White; gold bands; multi coloured prints "Joshua Tetley Maltster"	177	20.00	30.00	15.00

THEAKSTON ALE

ASHTRAY, 1990-1995

Photograph not available
at press time

Backstamp: "Wade P D M Made in England"

No.	Description	Colourways	Shape/Size	U.S.$	Can.$	U.K.£
1.	Ashtray	White; black lettering "Theakston Traditional Ale"	Round/140	15.00	20.00	8.00

THORNE'S SCOTCH WHISKY

WATER JUGS

Backstamp: **A.** "Reginald Corfield Limited Redhill Surrey," "Wade Regicor England"
B. Red printed "Wade Regicor" in circle and gold printed "Blended Scotch Whisky 86.8 Proof Blended and Bottled in Scotland and Imported in the Bottle by Hiram Walker Importers INC. Detroit. Mich."

No.	Description	Colourways	Shape/Size	U.S.$	Can.$	U.K.£
1.	Water Jug, ice-check spout	White; black lettering "Thorne's 10 yr old Scotch"	Oval/165	30.00	35.00	15.00
2.	Water Jug, ice-check spout	White; gold crest; black/gold lettering "Thorne's Scotch"	Oval/175	35.00	40.00	18.00

THORNTON AND FRANCE SHERRY

BARREL, 1980

This barrel has a wooden tap and sits on a stand. The lettering is on the front of the barrel.

Photograph not available
at press time

Backstamp: "Royal Victoria Pottery Staffordshire Wade England"

No.	Description	Colourways	Size	U.S.$	Can.$	U.K.£
1.	Barrel	Brown; gold bands, lettering "Thornton & France produce of Spain Sherry"	224	145.00	190.00	95.00

THRELFALLS

ASHTRAY

Backstamp: Printed circular "Reginald Corfield Limited, Redhill Surrey" with "Regicor Wade England" through the circle (1968-1969)

No.	Description	Colourways	Shape/Size	U.S.$	Can.$	U.K.£
1.	Ashtray	Cream; gold & red tankard print; red lettering "Threlfalls"	Square/140	12.00	15.00	6.00

TIA MARIA JAMAICAN LIQUEUR

WATER JUGS, 1969-1984

The No. 1 jug has an ice-check spout; No. 2 has a recessed handle and an open spout.

Photograph not available
at press time

Backstamp: "Wade pdm England" (PDM joined 1969-1984)

No.	Description	Colourways	Shape/Size	U.S.$	Can.$	U.K.£
1.	Water Jug	Black; gold lettering "Tia Maria Liqueur"	Rectangular/165	25.00	30.00	12.00
2.	Water Jug	Dark brown; yellow lettering "Tia Maria The Jamaican Liqueur"	Round/114	25.00	30.00	12.00
3.	Water Jug	Dark brown, yellow lettering "Tia Maria The Jamaican Liqueur"	Round/70 Miniature	35.00	45.00	18.00

TOBERMORY WHISKY

DECANTERS, 1995-1996

The bottle-shaped decanter was first produced in 1993 in a limited edition of 1,500 (24 of which were presented to Her Majesty Queen Elizabeth II). The Tobermory bottle decanter is all white with a black transfer print on the front of a ferry boat.

Photographs not available
at press time

Backstamp: Unknown

No.	Description	Colourways	Size	U.S.$	Can.$	U.K.£
1.	Bottle Decanter	White; black print/lettering "Tobermory Isle of Mull Finest Scotch Whisky"	305	60.00	80.00	30.00
2.	Decanter	White; black/gold lettering "Tobermory Whisky"	305	60.00	80.00	30.00

TREBLE GOLD

ASHTRAY, 1955-1962

This ashtray has a print on it of a horseshoe.

Photograph not available
at press time

Backstamp: "Wade Regicor, London England," laurel leaves, large size

No.	Description	Colourways	Shape/Size	U.S.$	Can.$	U.K.œ
1.	Ashtray	Pale green; red/white print; red lettering "Treble Gold"	Rectangular/225	10.00	15.00	5.00

TRELAWNEY'S PRIDE REAL CASK ALE

TANKARD

Backstamp: Red printed "Wade PDM" with two lines

No.	Description	Colourways	Shape/Size	U.S.$	Can.$	U.K.£
1.	Tankard	White; gold rims; black print, lettering "Trelawney's Pride 1650 - 1727 Alc 4.4% Vol Real Cask Ale Twenty Thousand Cornish Men Will Know The Reason Why"	Round/115	20.00	25.00	12.00

TUBORG PILSENER

WATER JUGS

Water Jug (No.2)

Backstamp: Red Printed "Wade pdm England" (PDM joined 1969-1984)

No.	Description	Colourways	Shape/Size	U.S.$	Can.$	U.K.£
1.	Water Jug	Dark green jug; white/gold/red lettering "Tuborg Pilsener & Tuborg Strong Lager Gold"	14 Rectangular	35.00	42.00	18.00
2.	Water Jug	Black jug; red/gold crown; gold/red lettering "Tuborg Strong Lager Gold"	155 Rectangular	35.00	42.00	18.00

TULLAMORE DEW IRISH WHISKEY
TULLAMORE DEW DISTILLERY

WATER JUG, 1994-1996

Photograph not available
at press time

Backstamp: "Wade p d m Made in England"

No.	Description	Colourways	Size	U.S.$	Can.$	U.K.£
1.	Water Jug, open spout	Black; white lettering "Tullamore Dew Finest Old Irish Whiskey"	Rectangular/133	25.00	30.00	12.00

USHER'S SCOTCH WHISKY

DRINK POURER AND WATER JUGS, 1955-1962

The No. 2 water jug has an extra long spout.

Water Jug

Drink Pourer

Backstamp **A.** Black printed "Wade Regicor, London England," laurel leaves, large size
B. Red printed "Wade PDM England" (pdm separated 1984-1990)
C. Impressed "C52A" under porcelain button, not seen unless pourer is taken apart

No.	Description	Colourways	Shape/Size	U.S.$	Can.$	U.K.£
1.	Drink Pourer	White/green; metal spout, neck; white lettering "Usher's Scotch Whisky"	C52A/40 x 48 Octagonal	25.00	30.00	12.00
2.	Water Jug	Cream; black lettering "Usher's Scotch Whisky"	Round/127	25.00	30.00	12.00
3.	Water Jug	Yellow; black lettering"Usher's Scotch Whisky"	Round/110	25.00	30.00	12.00
4.	Water jug	White; green lettering "Usher's Scotch Whisky"	Round/125	30.00	35.00	15.00

VAT 69 SCOTCH WHISKY

ASHTRAYS AND WATER JUGS, 1955-1980

The jugs have an open spout and recessed handles.

Ashtray (No.1)

Ashtray (No.3)

Water Jug (No.6)

Backstamp: **A.** "Wade Regicor, London England," laurel leaves, large size
B. "Reginald Corfield Limited Redhill Surrey," "Wade Regicor England"
C. "Wade pdm England"
D. "Wade Regicor Made in UK"

No.	Description	Colourways	Shape/Size	U.S.$	Can.$	U.K.£
1.	Ashtray	Black; white/gold lettering "Vat 69 Finest Scotch Whisky"	Round/101	15.00	20.00	8.00
2.	Ashtray	White/light blue; black/gold lettering "Vat 69 Scotch Whisky"	Round/101	15.00	20.00	8.00
3.	Ashtray	White/dark blue; black/gold lettering "Vat 69 Scotch Whisky"	Round/101	15.00	20.00	8.00
4.	Ashtray	Blue; white lettering "Vat 69"	Square/140	15.00	20.00	8.00
5.	Ashtray	Dark blue; white lettering "Vat 69"	Square/140 clipped corners	15.00	20.00	8.00
6.	Water Jug	Black; white lettering "Finest Scotch Whisky Vat 69"	Round/108	30.00	35.00	15.00
7.	Water Jug	Black; white/gold lettering "Vat 69"	Round/108	30.00	35.00	15.00

DRINK POURERS

The drink pourers, shape C53, have a straight base.

Drink Pourer (No.1)

Backstamp: Printed "Wade Regicor Made in UK"

No.	Description	Colourways	Shape/size	U.S.$	Can.$	U.K.£
1.	Drink Pourer	Black; all porcelain; white lettering "Vat 69"	Circular/117	25.00	30.00	15.00
2.	Drink Pourer	Black; plastic spout & neck; white lettering "Vat 69"	Oval/40 x 44	25.00	30.00	10.00
3.	Drink Pourer	Cream: Porcelain tube; gold line; white lettering "Vat 69"	Circular/41	30.00	35.00	15.00
			Circular/41			
4.	Drink Pourer	Cream; porcelain tube; golf lettering "Vat 69"	Circular/41	30.00	35.00	15.00

VAUX BREWERIES

ASHTRAY, 1969-1984

Backstamp: "Wade pdm England"

No.	Description	Colourways	Shape/Size	U.S.$	Can.$	U.K.£
1.	Ashtray	Amber; red label; white lettering "Vaux"	Tankard/177	30.00	38.00	16.00

BEER STEIN

Vaux School Of Sport, 1983

The one-pint Vaux School of Sport Stein was issued in 1983. It has purple lustre bands around the rim and several transfer prints of various sports with the words, 21st Anniversary Vaux Sportsman and Sportswoman of the Year Vaux School of Sport Lorimer & Clark Edinburgh, Liefmans Oudenaarde, Fred Koch New York State, Vaux Sunderland, Wards Sheffield, Darleys Doncaster 1983 Limited Edition.

Photograph not available
at press time

Backstamp: A. "Wade pdm England"
          B. Transfer printed "Wade p d m England" (PDM separate 1984-1990)

No.	Name	Colourways	Size	U.S.$	Can.$	U.K.£
1.	1983 School of Sport	White; purple lustre bands; grey/green/red prints	155	65.00	85.00	30.00

LOVING CUPS, MUGS, AND TANKARDS, 1977-1995

Since 1977 Wade PDM at the Wade Heath Pottery (now known as the Hilltop Site of Wade Ceramics) has produced seasonal loving cups, mugs and tankards for Vaux Breweries. They were presented as Christmas gifts to valued clients of the brewery. Most of these tankards differ from those usually associated with Wade in that they are shaped more like a tall mug with a wide mouth.

Loving Cup

In 1982 Wade produced a two-handled, half-pint loving cup for Vaux, called the "Soldiers of the Maxim Gun Detachment Loving Cup." It has a purple lustre decoration on the rim and handles and a transfer print on the front of the Maxim Gun Detachment (Ernest Vaux was a colonel in this detachment, which fought in the Boer War).

Backstamp: "Wade p d m England"

No.	Name	Colourways	Size	U.S.$	Can.$	U.K.£
1.	The Soldiers of the Maxim Gun Detachment 1982	White; purple lustre; grey-green print	½ pint/83	50.00	70.00	25.00

Mugs

1978: Sunderland Draught Bitter Mug has an ornamental label with purple lustre bands.
1981: The Vaux company logos mug has purple shields displaying the names and logos of the companies in the Vaux Group.
1984: Vaux Delivery Lorries : Purple lustre bands and transfer prints of brewery delivery lorries decorate this mug.
1985: Eagle Head: On the front of this mug is an eagle's head on a gold medallion, and a history of the Vaux group is listed on the back.
1986: Vaux brewery 1910: A nice print of Vaux Brewery workers standing in of the Vaux courtyard c.1910.
1987: Vaux Fine Ales & Lagers: A brewery label decorates the front with information on ales and lagers on the back.
1988: The Double Maxim Premium Quality: Double Maxim label on the front and the text on the back recounts the history of Maxim Ale, first produced to mark the homecoming of Colonel Vaux from the Boer War.
1989: The Maxim Light: Maxim Light label on the front and Vaux Brewery information on the back.
1991: More Choice More Vaux: Gold leaf decoration and glasses of Vaux Ales decorate this mug.
1992: Two mugs were produced. One was the 1992 City of Sunderland to mark the change of Sunderland from a town to a city, decorated with coats of arms and Vaux Fine Ales and Lager labels. The other was the 1992 Pub Signs; Vaux Breweries A-Z Good Pub Guide is printed on this mug along with Popular English pub signs and decorations.
1993: The Samson Special: A Samson Special Label on the front and the history and virtues of ale on the back.
1994: The Taste of Tradition: Decorated with pump handles and pump clips of Vaux ales and lagers.
1995: A New Double Maxim : This new Double Maxim ale was produced for Christmas 1985 decorated with the New Double Maxim label on the front and the back recounts the history of the brew.

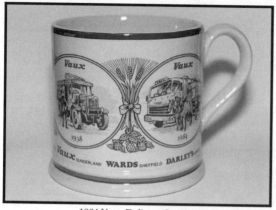

1984 Vaux Delivery Lorries

1986 Vaux Brewery 1910

1988 Double Maxim

Backstamp: **A.** "Wade pdm England"
B. "Wade P D M Made in England"

No.	Name	Colourways	Size	U.S.$	Can.$	U.K.£
1.	1978 Sunderland Draught	White; purple lustre; red/black "Sunderland Draught Bitter Vaux"	Pint/108	70.00	90.00	35.00
2.	1981 Vaux Logos	White; purple lustre; grey-green logos, lettering	Pint/108	50.00	70.00	25.00
3.	1984 Vaux Delivery Lorries	White; purple lustre; grey-green/ yellow-brown prints, red lettering	Pint/108	70.00	90.00	35.00
4.	1985 Eagle Head	White; gold lustre eagle; black lettering	Pint/108	70.00	90.00	35.00
5.	1986 Vaux Brewery 1910	White; purple lustre; black print, lettering "Vaux Brewery 1910"	Pint/108	75.00	95.00	40.00
6.	1987 Vaux Fine Ales and Lagers	White; gold bands; black/red/gold label, lettering "Fine Ales & Lagers Vaux Breweries Ltd"	Pint/108	70.00	90.00	35.00
7.	1988 Double Maxim	White; gold bands; red/brown/white label "Double Maxim"	Pint/108	70.00	90.00	35.00
8.	1989 Maxim Light	White; gold bands/stripes; gold/red/white "Maxim Light"	Pint/108	70.00	90.00	35.00
9.	1991 More Choice	White; gold decoration; multi-coloured print "More Choice More Vaux"	Pint/108	75.00	95.00	40.00

1992 City of Sunderland, 1994 Taste of Tradition

1995 Double Maxim, 1993 Samson Special Premium

1995 Double Maxim

No.	Name	Colourways	Size	U.S.$	Can.$	U.K.£
10.	1992 City of Sunderland	White; multi-coloured print, black lettering	Pint/108	70.00	90.00	35.00
11.	1992 Vaux Breweries Pub Signs	White; gold lustre; multi-coloured prints "Vaux Breweries A-Z Good Pub Guide 1992"	Pint/108	70.00	90.00	35.00
12.	1993 Samson Special	White; gold bands; yellow/red/black label, lettering "Samson Special Premium Bitter"	Pint/108	70.00	90.00	35.00
13.	1994 Taste of Tradition	White; gold bands; multi-coloured prints "Taste of Tradition"	Pint/108	70.00	90.00	35.00
14.	1995 Double Maxim	White; gold bands; gold/black/brown/red label "Double Maxim"	Pint/108	70.00	90.00	35.00

Tankards

The Tavern Tankard, produced in 1977, resembles an early 18th century pewter tankard. The Lorimer's Beers Tankard produced in 1979, is a pint-size traditional tankard with a leaf thumb rest on the handle. It is decorated with a print of a Lorimer's Beers label with sheaves of barley and corn. The Vaux tankard for 1980 was produced by another pottery. In 1981 Wade was back again, issuing the Vaux Logos Mug, which is decorated with shields, inside which are the Vaux Company names and logos.

The SH Ward 150th Anniversary tankard produced in 1990 is a traditional pint tankard with a leaf-shaped thumb rest. It is decorated with a print of a horse-drawn delivery dray leaving the brewery.

1979 Lorimer's (front)

1979 Lorimer's (back)

SH Ward 150 th Anniversary (front)

SH Ward 150th Anniversary (back)

Backstamp: A. "Wade pdm England" (pdm joined 1969-1984)
B. "Wade P D M Made in England"
C. "Green printed This tankard is one of a limited edition produced by Wade Potteries to commemorate the 150th Anniversary of S.H. Ward & Co Ltd. 1990"

No.	Name	Colourways	Size	U.S.$	Can.$	U.K.£
1.	1977 Gold Tavern	Gold lustre	127	50.00	70.00	25.00
2.	1979 Lorimer's	White; black/green label, print "Lorimer's Beers"	Pint/120	50.00	70.00	25.00
3.	1979 Lorimer's Beers	White; black	Traditional/110	45.00	55.00	35.00
4.	SH Ward 150th Anniversary	White; gold bands; green/black/yellow print	Pint/115	50.00	70.00	25.00
5.	1990 SH Ward 150th Anniversary	White; multi-coloured print of horse drawn delivery dray; black lettering	Traditional/120	50.00	70.00	30.00

V - J GIN

WATER JUGS, 1969-1984

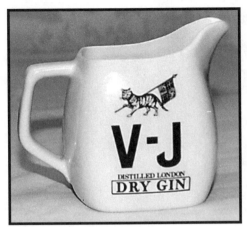

Water Jug (No.1)

Water Jug (No.2)

Backstamp A. "Wade pdm England"
B. Black printed "Wade Regicor London England," in a laurel leaf frame (large size 18 x 20mm 1953-1962)

No.	Description	Colourways	Shape/Size	U.S.$	Can.$	U.K.£
1.	Water Jug, open spout	White; black print; red/black lettering "V - J Distilled London Dry Gin"	Square/114	30.00	35.00	15.00
2.	Water Jug, ice-check spout	Cream; black tiger print; red/black lettering "Imported from England"	Round/165	30.00	35.00	18.00

VLADIVAR VODKA

DRINK POURER

Backstamp: Impressed "5455/1" on underside of button

No.	Description	Colourways	Shape/Size	U.S.$	Can.$	U.K.£
1.	Drink Pourer	White/red panel; plastic spout, neck; black/white lettering "Vladivar Vodka"	5455/1 40 x 47 Octagonal	25.00	30.00	10.00

WALKER'S DE LUXE BOURBON

DRINK POURER

Backstamp: Impressed "5455/1" under porcelain button seen when pourer is taken apart

No.	Description	Colourways	Shape/Size	U.S.$	Can.$	U.K.£
1.	Drink Pourer	White; plastic spout, tube; black lettering "Walker's de Luxe Bourbon"	5455/1 40 x 47 Octagonal	25.00	30.00	10.00

WARWICKS

ASHTRAY

Backstamp: Green printed "Wade - Regicor London England," in laurel leaf frame (small size 13 x 13 mm 1962-1968)

No.	Description	Colourways	Shape/size	U.S.$	Can.$	U.K.£
1.	Ashtray	White; black print/lettering "Warwicks Milkmaid Stout"	Round/133	12.00	15.00	8.00

WATNEYS BREWERIES

ASHTRAYS, 1955-1984

Ashtray (No.1)

Ashtray (No.2)

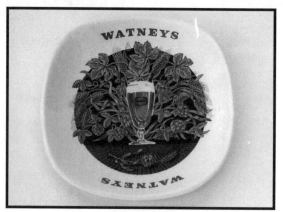

Ashtray (No.4)

Backstamp **A.** "Wade pdm England"
B. Black printed "Wade Regicor London England," in laurel leaf frame (large size 18 x 20 mm 1953-1962)

No.	Description	Colourways	Shape/Size	U.S.$	Can.$	U.K.œ
1.	Ashtray	Green; cream lettering "Watneys Special"	D-Shaped/190	30.00	35.00	15.00
2.	Ashtray	Purple; white/yellow lettering "Watneys Special Bitter"	Round/127	15.00	20.00	8.00
3.	Ashtray	Cream; red lettering "Watneys Straight Eight"	Round/140	15.00	20.00	8.00
4.	Ashtray	Cream; multi coloured barley and hops print; red lettering "Watneys"	Square/133	12.00	15.00	8.00
5.	Ashtray	Green; white/red lettering "Straight Eight"	Round/153	15.00	20.00	8.00
6.	Ashtray	Black; red lettering "Watneys"	Square/146	15.00	20.00	8.00
7.	Ashtray	Dark red; red/white lettering "Watneys Red"	Square/153	15.00	20.00	8.00

BAR LAMP, c.1979

This unusual dome-shaped lamp was produced to decorate public houses while advertising Watneys Breweries.

Backstamp: "Wade pdm England"

No.	Description	Colourways	Size	U.S.$	Can.$	U.K.£
1.	Bar Lamp	Green; yellow/brown lettering "Watneys Special Bitter"	250	160.00	240.00	80.00

WATSON'S SCOTCH WHISKY

DRINK POURER

Backstamp: None

No.	Description	Colourways	Shape/Size	U.S.$	Can.$	U.K.£
1.	Drink Pourer	White; metal spout, neck; black/red lettering "Watson's No.10 Scotch Whisky"	Round C53/41 x44	25.00	30.00	12.00

WHITBREAD ALES

ASHTRAYS, 1955-1962

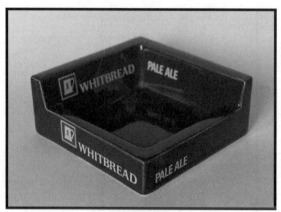

Ashtray (No.2)

Backstamp: A. "Wade Regicor, London England," laurel leaves, large size
B. Transfer print "Wade pdm England" (pdm joined 1969-1984)

No.	Description	Colourways	Shape/Size	U.S.$	Can.$	U.K.£
1.	Ashtray	White; black lettering "Whitbread"	Oval/171	15.00	20.00	8.00
2.	Ashtray	Dark blue; red/white tankard print; white lettering "Whitbread Pale Ale"	Square/115	10.00	12.00	6.00

BADGE, 1987

Wade produced a limited edition of 3,000 of these reclining frogs, then they were sent to Enterprise Products, where they were mounted on a tin badge over a picture of a water-lily pad. The words Whitbread Hopper are also on the badge. The frog often came unglued from the badge and can be found unmounted. It can be identified by its flat back and a 5-millimetre diameter hole in the centre.

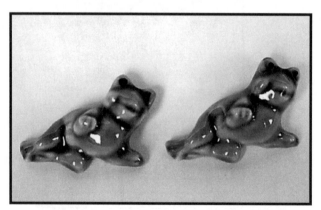

No.	Description	Colourways	Size	U.S.$	Can.$	U.K.£
1.	Frog Badge	White badge; green lily pad, frog; black eyes	14 x 55	40.00	45.00	20.00
2.	Frog (loose)	Green; black eyes	9 x 39	20.00	30.00	10.00

DECANTERS, 1979

In December 1978 Whitbread International, Belgium, commissioned Wade Heath to produce a limited quantity of Train Decanters to promote its pale ale. They resemble an American-style steam train with a cattle scoop on the front and the cork in the nose. The production run lasted from only February to March 1979, and 140 trains and 70 tenders were issued. After production ceased George Wade and Son Ltd. destroyed the moulds in agreement with the contract with Whitbread Breweries.

Backstamp: "Wade pdm England"

No.	Description	Colourways	Size	U.S.$	Can.$	U.K.£
1.	Train	Dark brown; pale cream/orange Whitbread label	205 x 115			
2.	Tender	Dark brown; pale cream/orange Whitbread label	130 x 105		Rare	
	Train and Tender					

WHITEHALL GIN

WATER JUG, 1969-1984

Backstamp: "Wade pdm England"

No.	Description	Colourways	Shape/Size	U.S.$	Can.$	U.K.£
1.	Water Jug, open spout	Pale blue; black print, black/red lettering "Whitehall London Dry Gin"	Square/114	25.00	30.00	12.00

WHITE HORSE SCOTCH WHISKY
UNITED DISTILLERS UK PLC

ASHTRAYS, 1955-1980

The ashtrays were produced between 1955 and 1980.

Ashtray (No.2)

Ashtray (No.3)

Ashtray (No.4)

Ashtray (No.5)

Backstamp: A. "Wade Regicor, London England," laurel leaves, large size
B. "Wade pdm England"
C. "Wade Regicor Made in UK"

No.	Description	Colourways	Shape/Size	U.S.$	Can.$	U.K.£
1.	Ashtray	Blue; white print; white lettering "White Horse"	Horseshoe/146	30.00	35.00	15.00
2.	Ashtray	Cream; black/white print; red lettering "White Horse"	Horseshoe/205	30.00	35.00	15.00
3.	Ashtray	Dark blue; white print, lettering "White Horse Scotch Whisky"	Square/140	10.00	15.00	5.00
4.	Ashtray	Black; white lettering "White Horse Scotch Whisky"	Square/140	10.00	15.00	5.00
5.	Ashtray	Royal blue; white horse print and lettering "White Horse Scotch Whisky"	Kidney/230	20.00	25.00	12.00

DRINK POURERS

There is no date known for the circular pourer with a straight base, shape C53. The White Horses Head Drink Pourer, produced in 1955, is the earliest known drink pourer produced by Wade. It is all porcelain. The date for the octagonal drink pourer, shape 5455/1, is unknown.

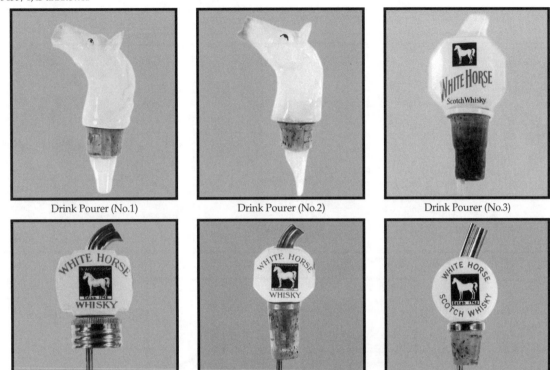

| Drink Pourer (No.1) | Drink Pourer (No.2) | Drink Pourer (No.3) |
| Drink Pourer (No.4) | Drink Pourer (No.5) | Drink Pourer (No.6) |

Backstamp: A. Impressed "C52A" under porcelain button not seen unless pourer is taken apart
B. Impressed "5455/1" under porcelain button not seen unless pourer is taken apart

No.	Description	Colourways	Shape/Size	U.S.$	Can.$	U.K.£
1.	Drink Pourer	White porcelain horse head; black eye	96	38.00	50.00	18.00
2.	Drink Pourer	White porcelain horse head; black eye	120	38.00	50.00	18.00
3.	Drink Pourer	White; plastic spout/tube ; black panel and white horse print; red/black lettering "White Horse Scotch Whisky"	5455/1 40 x 47 Octagonal	25.00	30.00	12.00
4.	Drink Pourer	White; metal spout/tube, screw cap; black panel and white horse print; red/white/ black lettering; lettering "White Horse The White Horse Cellar Estab 1742 Whisky"	52A/40 x 48 Rectangular	25.00	30.00	15.00
5.	Drink Pourer	White; metal spout/tube; black panel and white horse print; red,/white/black lettering "White Horse The White Horse Cellar Estab 1742 Whisky"	52A/40 x 48 Rectangular	25.00	30.00	12.00
6.	Drink Pourer	White; metal spout/tube ; black panel and white horse print; red/black lettering "White Horse Estab 1742 Scotch Whisky"	C52A/40 x 48 Octagonal	25.00	30.00	12.00

WATER JUGS, 1984-1990

These jugs have prints of a horse on them, except for No. 2, which has a print of the bottle label on it and No. 3, which has a framed print of a horses head. One of the jugs depicts a more unique approach to the theme: a white horse is depicted standing under an umbrella. Styles No. 1 and 2 have ice-check spouts; No. 6 has no handle and an open spout; style No. 4 has an open spout. The miniature water jug is so small we included a model of the Wade Cairn Terrier for comparison. The jug has an open spout. The backstamp is unusual, as it has only been found on 2 or 3 items. Date of production is believed to be early 1953.

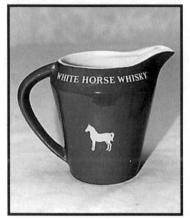
Water Jug (No.1)

Water Jug (No.3)

Water Jug (No.5)

Water Jug (No.5)

Backstamp: **A.** "Reginald Corfield Limited Redhill Surrey," "Wade Regicor England"
B. "Wade p d m England"
C. Red printed "Wade Regicor made in England" (in three straight lines)

No.	Description	Colourways	Shape/Size	U.S.$	Can.$	U.K.£
1.	Water Jug	Blue; white print, lettering "White Horse Whisky"	Round/133	25.00	35.00	20.00
2.	Water Jug	White; yellow/red/black print, lettering "White Horse Whisky"	Round/140	25.00	35.00	20.00
3.	Water Jug	Black; white/gold print; white lettering "White Horse Scotch"	Round/179	25.00	35.00	20.00
4.	Water Jug	Black; white print, label, lettering "White Horse Whisky"	Round/140	25.00	35.00	20.00
5.	Water Jug	Blue; white lettering "White Horse Scotch Whisky"	Round/60	25.00	35.00	20.00
6.	Water Jug	Cream; multi-coloured horse print; black lettering "Scotch And Water"	Round/140	40.00	55.00	25.00

WHYTE & MACKAY SCOTCH WHISKY

DECANTERS, 1983, 1990

Three types of Pot Still decanters were produced for Whyte & Mackay by Wade PDM between 1983 and 1990. Two were produced with a 22-carat gold glaze, and the third had a deep brown glaze. There is a slight size difference in the two gold decanters and in the size of the medallion on the front of the decanter: the first has a 55 mm medallion, the second a 50 mm medallion.

Pot Still (No.1)

Pot Still (No.3)

Decanter (No.4)

No.1 (Left); No.2 (Right)

Backstamp:
- **A.** "Wade p d m England"
- **B.** "Whyte & MacKay Scotland"
- **C.** Gold printed "Wade pdm England" (pdm joined 1969-1984)
- **D.** Gold Printed "Wade pdm England" (pdm separate 1984-1990)

No.	Name	Colourways	Size	U.S.$	Can.$	U.K.£
1.	Pot Still	Gold; embossed "Whyte & Mackay"	55 mm/250	55.00	65.00	35.00
2.	Pot Still	Gold; embossed "Whyte & Mackay"	50 mm/245	55.00	65.00	35.00
3.	Pot Still	Brown; embossed "Dalmore Whyte & Mackay"	50 mm/245	45.00	55.00	25.00
4.	Decanter	Royal Blue; gold print "Whyte & Mackay"	235	45.00	55.00	25.00

304

Water Jug (No.1)   Water Jug (No.2)

Backstamp: Printed "Wade pdm England" (pdm separated 1984-1990)

No.	Description	Colourways	Shape/Size	U.S.$	Can.$	U.K.£
1.	Water Jug ice-check spout	Cream; red print; brown lettering "Whyte & MacKay Scotch Whisky"	Round/177	25.00	30.00	12.00
2.	Water Jug, open spout	Cream; gold panel; red lion print; black/red lettering "Whyte & MacKay Double Lion Brand Special Scotch Whisky"	Rectangular/164	30.00	35.00	18.00

WILD TURKEY KENTUCKY STRAIGHT BOURBON WHISKY

DRINK POURER

No.	Description	Colourways	Shape/Size	U.S.$	Can.$	U.K.£
1.	Drink Pourer	White; metal spout, tube; black lettering "Wild Turkey"	Round/C53/ 41 x 44	30.00	35.00	12.00

WILLIAM THE CONQUEROR SCOTCH WHISKY

WATER JUG

Backstamp: Printed "Wade pdm England" (pdm joined 1969-1984)

No.	Description	Colourways	Shape/Size	U.S.$	Can.$	U.K.£
1.	Water Jug	Black; beige brown panel; black portrait; black/brown lettering "William The Conqueror Premium Scotch Whisky Product of Scotland"	Rectangular/165	35.00	40.00	18.00

WLS LTD. TORQUAY

DECANTER

This particular Panda model has a circular hole in the base resembling that seen on the "Cockatoo" and "Penguin" decanters. There is a black and gold paper label on the back of the model that reads "British Apricot Wine. Not less than 26% proof spirit. WLS Ltd Torquay."

Decanter (front)

Decanter (back)

Decanter (Base)

Backstamp: Black and gold paper label "British Apricot Wine. Not less than 26% proof spirit. WLS Ltd Torquay"

No.	Description	Colourways	Size	U.S.$	Can.$	U.K.£
1.	Panda, seated	Black/white; black/gold paper label	165	60.00	80.00	40.00

WOLFSCHMIDT VODKA

DRINK POURER

No.	Description	Colourways	Shape/size	U.S.$	Can.$	U.K.£
1.	Drink Pourer	White /red /black; metal spout, neck white/red lettering "Since; 1847 Wolf Schmidt Vodka"	C54/37 x 60 Rectangular	30.00	35.00	15.00

WORTHINGTON

ASHTRAYS

This E-shaped ashtray resembles the E-shaped jug, minus the handle, and is silver and blue.

Ashtray (No.2)

Ashtray (No.3)

Backstamp: A. "Wade Regicor, London England," laurel leaves, large size
B. "Wade pdm England"
C. Transfer print "Wade pdm England" (pdm joined 1969-1984)

No.	Description	Colourways	Size	U.S.$	Can.$	U.K.£
1.	Round	White/blue; blue lettering "You're Twice the Man on Worthington"	140	15.00	20.00	8.00
2.	Round	White; blue rim and lettering "Worthington"	140	15.00	20.00	8.00
3.	E-shaped	Blue/silver	140	36.00	48.00	20.00

BAR CIGARETTE LIGHTER

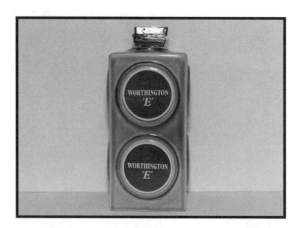

Backstamp: Printed "Wade pdm England" (pdm joined 1969-1984)

No.	Description	Colourways	Shape/size	U.S.$	Can.$	U.K.£
1.	Bar Cigarette Lighter	Amber; dark green; white lettering "Worthington E"	Rectangular/160	75.00	95.00	40.00

WATER JUGS, 1955-1984

The water jugs were issued between 1969 and 1984. The triangular jug has an ice-check spout. The E-shaped jug, which has an open spout, looks like the letter *E* when facing right. On the back "Worthington" is spelled backwards, so that when the jug is standing in front of a bar mirror, the name can be read.

Water Jug (No.1)

Backstamp: Printed "Wade pdm England" (pdm joined 1969-1984)

No.	Description	Colourways	Shape/Size	U.S.$	Can.$	U.K.£
1.	Water Jug	Blue/white; blue lettering "Worthington"	E-shaped/140	50.00	70.00	25.00
2.	Water Jug	Dark green; gold rim; blue/white lettering "Worthington"	Triangular/165	25.00	30.00	12.00

WYBOROWA VODKA

DRINK POURER

No.	Description	Colourways	Shape/size	U.S.$	Can.$	U.K.£
1.	Drink Pourer	White; metal spout, neck; red knight print; blue/red lettering "Trade Mark Wodka Wyborowa Imported From Poland"	C62/47 x 41 Rectangular	25.00	30.00	12.00

YE MONKS CURIOUS OLD WHISKY
DONALD FISHER

WATER JUG

Backstamp: Red printed "Wade pdm Made in England" (pdm joined 1969-1984)

No.	Description	Colourways	Size	U.S.$	Can.$	U.K.£
1.	Water Jug, open spout	Amber jug; black print/lettering "Ye Monks Curious Old Whisky Donald Fisher"	110	45.00	55.00	25.00

ZAMOYSKI VODKA

ASHTRAY

Backstamp: Printed circular "Wade P D M" (p d m separated 1984-1990)

No.	Description	Colourways	Shape/Size	U.S.$	Can.$	U.K.£
1.	Ashtray	Black; white lettering "Zamoyski Pure Vodka"	Round/155	8.00	12.00	4.00

ANONYMOUS LIQUOR PRODUCTS

Between 1954 and 1995 Wade Regicor and Wade PDM produced hundreds of different products advertising various brands of liquor. The companies that commissioned the following liquor products are unknown.

DECANTERS

Bottle Decanters, 1993-1994

The Sauternes, Sherry and Vin Rose decanters were produced in 1993 in a limited edition of 1,500 (500 of each version). Twenty-four of them (four of each version) were presented to Queen Elizabeth. In 1994 more decanters were produced: Burgundy, Claret and Port. The transfer print on the front is of two cherubs on a wreath with the name of the drink in gold letters in the centre.

Right (No.5); Left (No.4)

Bottle Decanter (No. 6)

Backstamp **A.** "Royal Victoria Pottery Wade England"
B. Printed "Royal Victoria Pottery Wade England"

No.	Description	Colourways	Size	U.S.$	Can.$	U.K.£
1.	Burgundy	White; black wreath; gold lettering	305	55.00	75.00	35.00
2.	Claret	White; burgundy wreath; gold lettering	305	55.00	75.00	35.00
3.	Port	Royal blue; gold wreath, lettering	305	55.00	75.00	35.00
4.	Sauternes	Creamy white; green wreath; gold lettering "Sauternes"	305	55.55	75.00	35.00
5.	Sherry	Yellow; gold wreath, lettering "Sherry"	305	55.00	75.00	35.00
6.	Vin Rose	Creamy white; pink wreath; gold lettering "Vin Rose"	305	55.00	75.00	35.00

Leaping Salmon Decanter, 1985-1986

It is believed that this decanter was produced for a Scottish distillery and was in production for a very short period of time. It has been found at antique shows minus its contents and labels.

Backstamp: "Wade"

No.	Description	Colourways	Size	U.S.$	Can.$	U.K.£
1.	Leaping Salmon	Pearlized grey/lilac; blue base	270	200.00	275.00	100.00

Mermaid Decanter

The commissioner of this mermaid decanter is unknown.

Backstamp: Gold Printed "Genuine Wade England"

No.	Description	Colourways	Size	U.S.$	Can.$	U.K.£
1.	Mermaid	White; gold hair, tail, starfish; white rock; blue waves	255	55.00	70.00	35.00

NOVELTY DRINK POURERS

Animal, Bird and Fish Drink Pourers, 1975-1982

Theseall porcelain novelty shaped drink pourers were produced by Wade Ireland. Those with more than two colours were produced first; later versions have only two colours shaded together.

Bush Baby

Eagle, with pointed spout

Eagle, rounded spout

Owl

Salmon

Songbird, pointed spout

Backstamp: Unmarked

No.	Description	Colourways	Size	U.S.$	Can.$	U.K.£
1.	Bush Baby	Beige/black; yellow eyes; green branch	120	90.00	100.00	45.00
2.	Bush Baby	Beige/grey	120	90.00	100.00	45.00
3.	Golden Eagle	Honey; light green breast, pointed spout	138	95.00	110.00	50.00
4.	Golden Eagle	Beige/grey, rounded spout	110	95.00	110.00	50.00
5.	Golden Eagle	Beige; blue grey wings; round spout	138	65.00	80.00	35.00
6.	Owl	Honey; green head, wings	110	95.00	110.00	50.00
7.	Owl	Beige; grey head, wings	110	95.00	110.00	50.00
8.	Salmon	Honey; mottled green tail, base	120	70.00	95.00	35.00
9.	Salmon	Beige/grey	120	70.00	95.00	35.00
10.	Salmon (Lg)	Honey/brown fish; blue/grey water; round spout	120	70.00	95.00	35.00
11.	Salmon (Sm)	Honey fish; honey/green water; pointed spout	100	60.00	70.00	25.00
12.	Songbird	Honey; dark brown tail; green branch; flat spout	120	70.00	95.00	35.00
13.	Songbird	Honey/grey-brown; pointed spout	98	70.00	95.00	35.00
14.	Songbird (Lg)	Pale green all over; round spout	120	75.00	80.00	50.00
15.	Songbird (Sm)	Honey/grey brown; round spout	98	95.00	120.00	60.00

No.	Description	Colourways	Shape/Size	U.S.$	Can.$	U.K.£
16.	Spaniel Puppy	Beige/grey; green base	110	110.00	125.00	60.00
17.	Squirrel	Beige/brown & grey on green base; round spout	98	65.00	80.00	30.00

Double Brand Drink Pourers

This pourer features two liquor manufacturers, one or either side: "Greenalls London Dry Gin" and "Vladivar Vodka."

Photograph not available
at press time

Backstamp: Impressed "5455/1" on underside of button.

No.	Description	Colourways	Shape/Size	U.S.$	Can.$	U.K.£
1.	Drink Pourer	Red/white; plastic tube, spout; on front "Greenhalls 1761 London Dry Gin" on back "Vladivar Vodka"	Octagonal/40 x 47	25.00	30.00	10.00

316

Horse Head Drink Pourer

This horse head pourer is very similar in shape to the White Horse Whisky pourer but the mane and the ear are slightly larger.

No.	Description	Colourways	Size	U.S.$	Can.$	U.K.£
1.	Drink Pourer	Horse's head; tan brown; black markings	125	45.00	55.00	25.00

Horse Head with Bridle Pourers, 1955

This drink pourer is from a different mould than the White Horse's Head Drink Pourer produced for White Horse Scotch Whisky. The horse depicted in this all-porcelain drink pourer is wearing a bridle, the head is further forward and the neck is shorter than that of the "White Horse's Head" model.

Drink Pourer (No.2)   Drink Pourer (No.3)

Backstamp: Unmarked

No.	Description	Colourways	Size	U.S.$	Can.$	U.K.£
1.	Drink Pourer	Blue; black eyes	110	45.00	50.00	25.00
2.	Drink Pourer	Blue	110	45.00	50.00	25.00
3.	Drink Pourer	Dark green	110	45.00	50.00	25.00

Plain Drink Pourers

Drink Pourer (No.1)

Drink Pourer (No.2)

Drink Pourer (No.3)

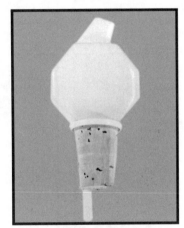

Drink Pourer (No.4)

Backstamp A. Impressed "C52A" under porcelain button, not seen unless pourer is taken apart
B. Impressed "5455/1" on underside of button
C. Printed "Wade Regicor London England," in laurel leaf frame (large size 18 x 20 mm 1953-1962)

No.	Description	Colourways	Shape/Size	U.S.$	Can.$	U.K.£
1.	Drink Pourer	White; metal spout, neck	Round C53 / 41 x 44	12.00	15.00	8.00
2.	Drink Pourer	White; all porcelain	AP2 / 117	12.00	15.00	8.00
3.	Drink Pourer	White; plastic spout, neck;	Octagonal C52A / 40 x 48	12.00	15.00	8.00
4.	Drink Pourer	White; plastic spout, neck;	Octagonal 5455/1 40 x 47	12.00	15.00	8.00

Playing Card Drink Pourers

The print on No. 1 is of the King of Diamonds, No. 2 the Queen of Clubs.

Photograph not available at press time

Backstamp: Unmarked

No.	Description	Colourways	Shape/Size	U.S.$	Can.$	U.K.£
1.	King of Diamonds	White; plastic tube; multi-coloured print	Rectangular/48	30.00	35.00	15.00
2.	Queen of Clubs	White; plastic tube; multi-coloured print	Rectangular/48	30.00	35.00	15.00

PUMP HANDLES

These beer pump handles were produced by Wade PDM between 1975 and 1985 for various breweries. The "Huntsmen" pump handles have a large print on the top and a smaller related print on the bottom.

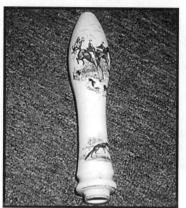

"Huntsmen and Fox"

No.3

No.4

No.5

No.7

No.8

Backstamp: Unmarked

No.	Description/colourways	Size	U.S.$	Can.$	U.K.£
1.	One huntsman on galloping horse, fox; running White; multi-coloured print	225	45.00	50.00	25.00
2.	Two huntsmen on galopping horses, seated fox; White; multi-coloured print	225	45.00	50.00	25.00
3.	Two huntsmen on galloping horses, hat, horn; White; multi-coloured print	225	45.00	50.00	25.00
4.	Three huntsmen on horses, hounds, fox running; White; multi-coloured print	225	45.00	50.00	25.00
5.	Three huntsmen Talking, fax walking; White; multi-coloured print	225	45.00	50.00	25.00
6.	Two huntsmen on horses, hat, horn, rein; White; multi-coloured print	225	45.00	50.00	25.00
7.	One huntsman on galloping horse, hat, horn, riding crop; White; multi-coloured print	225	45.00	50.00	25.00
8.	Plough horses; White; multi-coloured print	225	45.00	50.00	25.00
9.	Grapes and vine leaves; White; green/yellow print	125	45.00	50.00	25.00

WATER JUGS

Advertising

This water jug has the names of four different drinks around the body and has an ice check spout.

No.	Description	Colourways	Size	U.S.$	Can.$	U.K.£
1.	Water Jug, Advertising	Black; gold rim; white lettering "Booth's Gin, Hine Cognac, Black & White Scotch Whisky, Cossack Vodka"	125 Round	30.00	40.00	20.00

Veteran Car Series

Round Jug, 1 1/2 Pint

Square Jug, 1/2 Pint

Triangular Jug, 1 1/2 Pint

Backstamp: "Wade England"

No.	Description	Colourways	Shape/Size	U.S.$	Can.$	U.K.£
1.	Bentley, 1 ½ pint	Pale yellow; multi-coloured print	Round/115	30.00	35.00	15.00
2.	Bentley, ½ pint	Pale yellow; multi-coloured print	Square/95	30.00	35.00	15.00
3.	Bentley, pint	Pale yellow; multi-coloured print	Square/105	30.00	35.00	15.00
4.	Bentley, 1 ½ Pint	Pale yellow; multi-coloured print	Triangular/150	30.00	35.00	15.00

WINE DECANTER LABEL

Shape No.: Impressed shape number "S52/3"

No.	Description	Colourways	Shape/Size	U.S.$	Can.$	U.K.£
1.	Wine Decanter Label	White; gold rim; green/brown print, green lettering "Chilled Dry White Wine"	Oval/76	10.00	15.00	5.00

INDEX